Eureka Math
Grade 7
Modules 1 & 2

Special thanks go to the Gordon A. Cain Center and to the Department of Mathematics at Louisiana State University for their support in the development of *Eureka Math*.

Published by the *non-profit* Great Minds

Copyright © 2016 Great Minds. No part of this work may be reproduced, sold, or commercialized, in whole or in part, without written permission from *Great Minds*. Non-commercial use is licensed pursuant to a Creative Commons Attribution-NonCommercial-ShareAlike 4.0 license; for more information, go to http://greatminds.net/maps/math/copyright. "Great Minds" and "Eureka Math" are registered trademarks of Great Minds.

ed in the U.S.A.

ook may be purchased from the publisher at eureka-math.org

8 7 6 5

8-1-63255-316-4

Lesson 1: An Experience in Relationships as Measuring Rate

Classwork

Example 1: How Fast Is Our Class?

Record the results from the paper-passing exercise in the table below.

Key Terms from Grade 6 Ratios and Unit Rates

A *ratio* is an ordered pair of numbers which are not both zero. A ratio is denoted $A:B$ to indicate the order of the numbers: the number A is first, and the number B is second.

Two ratios $A:B$ and $C:D$ are *equivalent ratios* if there is a nonzero number c such that $C = cA$ and $D = cB$. For example, two ratios are equivalent if they both have values that are equal.

A ratio relationship between two types of quantities, such as 5 miles per 2 hours, can be described as a *rate* (i.e., the quantity 2.5 miles/hour).

The numerical part of the rate is called the *unit rate* and is simply the value of the ratio, in this case 2.5. This means that in 1 hour the car travels 2.5 miles. The *unit* for the rate is miles/hour, read miles per hour.

Trial	Number of Papers Passed	Time (in seconds)	Ratio of Number of Papers Passed to Time	Rate	Unit Rate
1					
2					
3					

Example 2: Our Class by Gender

	Number of Boys	Number of Girls	Ratio of Boys to Girls
Class 1			
Class 2			
Whole 7th Grade			

Create a pair of equivalent ratios by making a comparison of quantities discussed in this Example.

Exercise 1: Which is the Better Buy?

Value-Mart is advertising a Back-to-School sale on pencils. A pack of 30 sells for $7.97, whereas a 12-pack of the same brand costs $4.77. Which is the better buy? How do you know?

©2016 Great Minds. eureka-math.org
G7-M1M2-SE-B1-1.3.1-02.2016

Lesson Summary

Unit rate is often a useful means for comparing ratios and their associated rates when measured in different units. The unit rate allows us to compare varying sizes of quantities by examining the number of units of one quantity per one unit of the second quantity. This value of the ratio is the unit rate.

Problem Set

1. Find each rate and unit rate.

   a. 420 miles in 7 hours

   b. 360 customers in 30 days

   c. 40 meters in 16 seconds

   d. $7.96 for 5 pounds

2. Write three ratios that are equivalent to the one given: The ratio of right-handed students to left-handed students is $18:4$.

3. Mr. Rowley has 16 homework papers and 14 exit tickets to return. Ms. Rivera has 64 homework papers and 60 exit tickets to return. For each teacher, write a ratio to represent the number of homework papers to number of exit tickets they have to return. Are the ratios equivalent? Explain.

4. Jonathan's parents told him that for every 5 hours of homework or reading he completes, he would be able to play 3 hours of video games. His friend Lucas's parents told their son that he could play 30 minutes for every hour of homework or reading time he completes. If both boys spend the same amount of time on homework and reading this week, which boy gets more time playing video games? How do you know?

5. Of the 30 girls who tried out for the lacrosse team at Euclid Middle School, 12 were selected. Of the 40 boys who tried out, 16 were selected. Are the ratios of the number of students on the team to the number of students trying out the same for both boys and girls? How do you know?

6. Devon is trying to find the unit price on a 6-pack of drinks on sale for $2.99. His sister says that at that price, each drink would cost just over $2.00. Is she correct, and how do you know? If she is not, how would Devon's sister find the correct price?

7. Each year Lizzie's school purchases student agenda books, which are sold in the school store. This year, the school purchased 350 books at a cost of $1,137.50. If the school would like to make a profit of $1,500 to help pay for field trips and school activities, what is the least amount they can charge for each agenda book? Explain how you found your answer.

This page intentionally left blank

Lesson 2: Proportional Relationships

Classwork .

Example 1: Pay by the Ounce Frozen Yogurt

A new self-serve frozen yogurt store opened this summer that sells its yogurt at a price based upon the total weight of the yogurt and its toppings in a dish. Each member of Isabelle's family weighed his dish, and this is what they found. Determine if the cost is proportional to the weight.

Weight (ounces)	12.5	10	5	8
Cost ($)	5	4	2	3.20

The cost _____ the weight.

Example 2: A Cooking Cheat Sheet

In the back of a recipe book, a diagram provides easy conversions to use while cooking.

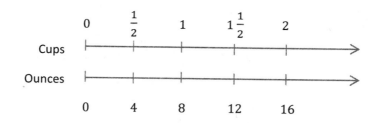

The ounces _____the cups.

Exercise 1

During Jose's physical education class today, students visited activity stations. Next to each station was a chart depicting how many calories (on average) would be burned by completing the activity.

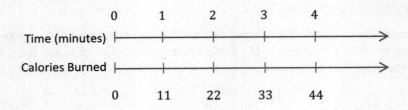

Calories Burned While Jumping Rope

a. Is the number of calories burned proportional to time? How do you know?

b. If Jose jumped rope for 6.5 minutes, how many calories would he expect to burn?

EUREKA
MATH™

Example 3: Summer Job

Alex spent the summer helping out at his family's business. He was hoping to earn enough money to buy a new $220 gaming system by the end of the summer. Halfway through the summer, after working for 4 weeks, he had earned $112. Alex wonders, "If I continue to work and earn money at this rate, will I have enough money to buy the gaming system by the end of the summer?"

To determine if he will earn enough money, he decided to make a table. He entered his total money earned at the end of Week 1 and his total money earned at the end of Week 4.

Week	0	1	2	3	4	5	6	7	8
Total Earnings		$28			$112				

a.   Work with a partner to answer Alex's question.

b.   Are Alex's total earnings proportional to the number of weeks he worked? How do you know?

Lesson Summary

Measures of one type of quantity are *proportional to* measures of a second type of quantity if there is a number k so that for every measure x of a quantity of the first type, the corresponding measure y of a quantity of the second type is given by kx; that is, $y = kx$. The number k is called the *constant of proportionality*.

A *proportional relationship* is a correspondence between two types of quantities such that the measures of quantities of the first type are proportional to the measures of quantities of the second type.

Note that proportional relationships and ratio relationships describe the same set of ordered pairs but in two different ways. Ratio relationships are used in the context of working with equivalent ratios, while proportional relationships are used in the context of rates.

In the example given below, the distance is *proportional to* time since each measure of distance, y, can be calculated by multiplying each corresponding time, t, by the same value, 10. This table illustrates a *proportional relationship* between time, t, and distance, y.

Time (h), t	0	1	2	3
Distance (km), y	0	10	20	30

Problem Set

1. A cran-apple juice blend is mixed in a ratio of cranberry to apple of 3 to 5.

   a. Complete the table to show different amounts that are proportional.

Amount of Cranberry			
Amount of Apple			

   b. Why are these quantities proportional?

2. John is filling a bathtub that is 18 inches deep. He notices that it takes two minutes to fill the tub with three inches of water. He estimates it will take 10 more minutes for the water to reach the top of the tub if it continues at the same rate. Is he correct? Explain.

©2016 Great Minds. eureka-math.org
G7-M1M2-SE-B1-1.3.1-02.2016

Lesson 3: Identifying Proportional and Non-Proportional Relationships in Tables

Classwork

Example

You have been hired by your neighbors to babysit their children on Friday night. You are paid $8 per hour. Complete the table relating your pay to the number of hours you worked.

Hours Worked	Pay
1	
2	
3	
4	
$4\frac{1}{2}$	
5	
6	
6.5	

Based on the table above, is the pay proportional to the hours worked? How do you know?

Exercises

For Exercises 1–3, determine if y is proportional to x. Justify your answer.

1. The table below represents the relationship of the amount of snowfall (in inches) in 5 counties to the amount of time (in hours) of a recent winter storm.

x Time (h)	y Snowfall (in.)
2	10
6	12
8	16
2.5	5
7	14

2. The table below shows the relationship between the cost of renting a movie (in dollars) to the number of days the movie is rented.

x Number of Days	y Cost (dollars)
6	2
9	3
24	8
3	1

©2016 Great Minds. eureka-math.org
G7-M1M2-SE-B1-1.3.1-02.2016

3. The table below shows the relationship between the amount of candy bought (in pounds) and the total cost of the candy (in dollars).

x Amount of Candy (pounds)	y Cost (dollars)
5	10
4	8
6	12
8	16
10	20

4. Randy is planning to drive from New Jersey to Florida. Every time Randy stops for gas, he records the distance he traveled in miles and the total number of gallons used.

    Assume that the number of miles driven is proportional to the number of gallons consumed in order to complete the table.

Gallons Consumed	2	4		8	10	12
Miles Driven	54		189	216		

Lesson Summary

A type of quantity is proportional to a second if there is a constant number such that the product of each measure of the first type and the constant is equal to the corresponding measure of the second type.

Steps to determine if quantities in a table are proportional to each other:

1. For each row (or column), calculate $\dfrac{B}{A}$ where A is the measure of the first quantity, and B is the measure of the second quantity.

2. If the value of $\dfrac{B}{A}$ is the same for each pair of numbers, then the quantities in the table are proportional to each other.

Problem Set

In each table, determine if y is proportional to x. Explain why or why not.

1.

x	y
3	12
5	20
2	8
8	32

2.

x	y
3	15
4	17
5	19
6	21

3.

x	y
6	4
9	6
12	8
3	2

4. Kayla made observations about the selling price of a new brand of coffee that sold in three different-sized bags. She recorded those observations in the following table:

Ounces of Coffee	6	8	16
Price in Dollars	2.10	2.80	5.60

   a. Is the price proportional to the amount of coffee? Why or why not?

   b. Use the relationship to predict the cost of a 20 oz. bag of coffee.

5. You and your friends go to the movies. The cost of admission is $9.50 per person. Create a table showing the relationship between the number of people going to the movies and the total cost of admission.

   Explain why the cost of admission is proportional to the amount of people.

6. For every 5 pages Gil can read, his daughter can read 3 pages. Let g represent the number of pages Gil reads, and let d represent the number of pages his daughter reads. Create a table showing the relationship between the number of pages Gil reads and the number of pages his daughter reads.

   Is the number of pages Gil's daughter reads proportional to the number of pages he reads? Explain why or why not.

©2016 Great Minds. eureka-math.org
G7-M1M2-SE-B1-1.3.1-02.2016

7. The table shows the relationship between the number of parents in a household and the number of children in the same household. Is the number of children proportional to the number of parents in the household? Explain why or why not.

Number of Parents	Number of Children
0	0
1	3
1	5
2	4
2	1

8. The table below shows the relationship between the number of cars sold and the amount of money earned by the car salesperson. Is the amount of money earned, in dollars, proportional to the number of cars sold? Explain why or why not.

Number of Cars Sold	Money Earned (in dollars)
1	250
2	600
3	950
4	1,076
5	1,555

9. Make your own example of a relationship between two quantities that is NOT proportional. Describe the situation, and create a table to model it. Explain why one quantity is not proportional to the other.

This page intentionally left blank

Lesson 4: Identifying Proportional and Non-Proportional Relationships in Tables

Classwork

Example: Which Team Will Win the Race?

You have decided to walk in a long-distance race. There are two teams that you can join. Team A walks at a constant rate of 2.5 miles per hour. Team B walks 4 miles the first hour and then 2 miles per hour after that.

Task: Create a table for each team showing the distances that would be walked for times of 1, 2, 3, 4, 5, and 6 hours. Using your tables, answer the questions that follow.

Team A	
Time (hours)	Distance (miles)

Team B	
Time (hours)	Distance (miles)

a.   For which team is distance proportional to time? Explain your reasoning.

b.   Explain how you know distance for the other team is not proportional to time.

c. At what distance in the race would it be better to be on Team B than Team A? Explain.

d. If the members on each team walked for 10 hours, how far would each member walk on each team?

e. Will there always be a winning team, no matter what the length of the course? Why or why not?

f. If the race is 12 miles long, which team should you choose to be on if you wish to win? Why would you choose this team?

g. How much sooner would you finish on that team compared to the other team?

EUREKA
MATH™

Exercises

1. Bella types at a constant rate of 42 words per minute. Is the number of words she can type proportional to the number of minutes she types? Create a table to determine the relationship.

Minutes	1	2	3	6	60
Number of Words					

2. Mark recently moved to a new state. During the first month, he visited five state parks. Each month after, he visited two more. Complete the table below, and use the results to determine if the number of parks visited is proportional to the number of months.

Number of Months	Number of State Parks
1	
2	
3	
	23

EUREKA
MATH™

Lesson 4:   Identifying Proportional and Non-Proportional Relationships in Tables

S.17

©2016 Great Minds. eureka-math.org
G7-M1M2-SE-B1-1.3.1-02.2016

3. The table below shows the relationship between the side length of a square and the area. Complete the table. Then, determine if the length of the sides is proportional to the area.

Side Length (inches)	Area (square inches)
1	1
2	4
3	
4	
5	
8	
12	

Problem Set

1. Joseph earns $15 for every lawn he mows. Is the amount of money he earns proportional to the number of lawns he mows? Make a table to help you identify the type of relationship.

Number of Lawns Mowed				
Earnings ($)				

2. At the end of the summer, Caitlin had saved $120 from her summer job. This was her initial deposit into a new savings account at the bank. As the school year starts, Caitlin is going to deposit another $5 each week from her allowance. Is her account balance proportional to the number of weeks of deposits? Use the table below. Explain your reasoning.

Time (in weeks)				
Account Balance ($)				

3. Lucas and Brianna read three books each last month. The table shows the number of pages in each book and the length of time it took to read the entire book.

Pages Lucas Read	208	156	234
Time (hours)	8	6	9

Pages Brianna Read	168	120	348
Time (hours)	6	4	12

a. Which of the tables, if any, shows a proportional relationship?

b. Both Lucas and Brianna had specific reading goals they needed to accomplish. What different strategies did each person employ in reaching those goals?

©2016 Great Minds. eureka-math.org
G7-M1M2-SE-B1-1.3.1-02.2016

This page intentionally left blank

Lesson 5: Identifying Proportional and Non-Proportional Relationships in Graphs

Classwork

Opening Exercise

Isaiah sold candy bars to help raise money for his scouting troop. The table shows the amount of candy he sold compared to the money he received.

x Candy Bars Sold	y Money Received ($)
2	3
4	5
8	9
12	12

Is the amount of candy bars sold proportional to the money Isaiah received? How do you know?

_____

_____

Exploratory Challenge/Examples 1–3: From a Table to a Graph

Example 1

Using the ratio provided, create a table that shows money received is proportional to the number of candy bars sold. Plot the points in your table on the grid.

x Candy Bars Sold	y Money Received ($)
2	3

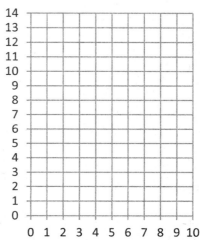

Important Note:

Characteristics of graphs of proportional relationships:

Example 2

Graph the points from the Opening Exercise.

x Candy Bars Sold	y Money Received ($)
2	3
4	5
8	9
12	12

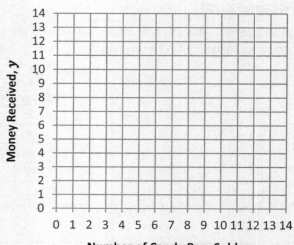

Example 3

Graph the points provided in the table below, and describe the similarities and differences when comparing your graph to the graph in Example 1.

x	y
0	6
3	9
6	12
9	15
12	18

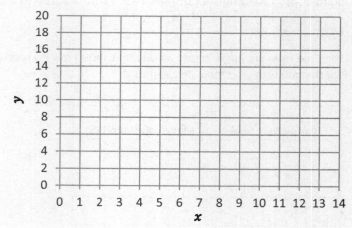

Similarities with Example 1:

Differences from Example 1:

EUREKA
MATH

Lesson Summary

When two proportional quantities are graphed on a coordinate plane, the points appear on a line that passes through the origin.

Problem Set

1. Determine whether or not the following graphs represent two quantities that are proportional to each other. Explain your reasoning.

a.

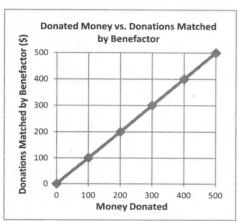

b.

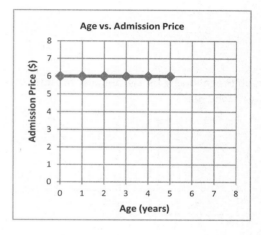

c.

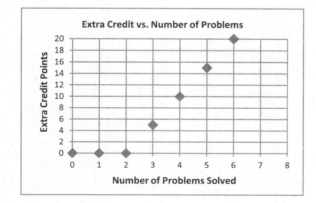

2. Create a table and a graph for the ratios 2: 22, 3 to 15, and 1: 11. Does the graph show that the two quantities are proportional to each other? Explain why or why not.

x	y

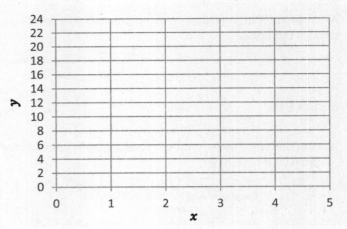

3. Graph the following tables, and identify if the two quantities are proportional to each other on the graph. Explain why or why not.

a.

x	y
3	1
6	2
9	3
12	4

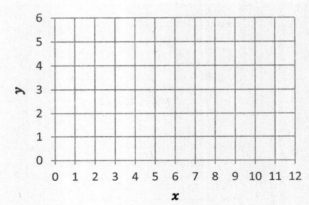

b.

x	y
1	4
2	5
3	6
4	7

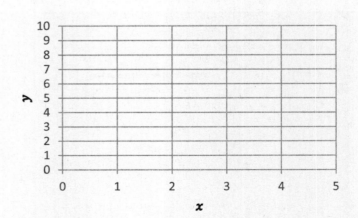

©2016 Great Minds. eureka-math.org
G7-M1M2-SE-B1-1.3.1-02.2016

Lesson 6: Identifying Proportional and Non-Proportional Relationships in Graphs

Classwork

Today's Exploratory Challenge is an extension of Lesson 5. You will be working in groups to create a table and graph and to identify whether the two quantities are proportional to each other.

Poster Layout

Use for notes

Problem:	Table:
Graph:	**Proportional or Not? Explanation:**

Gallery Walk

Take notes and answer the following questions:

- Were there any differences found in groups that had the same ratios?
- Did you notice any common mistakes? How might they be fixed?
- Were there any groups that stood out by representing their problem and findings exceptionally clearly?

<u>Poster 1:</u>

<u>Poster 2:</u>

<u>Poster 3:</u>

<u>Poster 4:</u>

©2016 Great Minds. eureka-math.org
G7-M1M2-SE-B1-1.3.1-02.2016

EUREKA
MATH™

Poster 5:

Poster 6:

Poster 7:

Poster 8:

Note about Lesson Summary:

Lesson Summary

The plotted points in a *graph of a proportional relationship* lie on a line that passes through the origin.

Problem Set

Sally's aunt put money in a savings account for her on the day Sally was born. The savings account pays interest for keeping her money in the bank. The ratios below represent the number of years to the amount of money in the savings account.

- After one year, the interest accumulated, and the total in Sally's account was $312.
- After three years, the total was $340. After six years, the total was $380.
- After nine years, the total was $430. After 12 years, the total amount in Sally's savings account was $480.

Using the same four-fold method from class, create a table and a graph, and explain whether the amount of money accumulated and the time elapsed are proportional to each other. Use your table and graph to support your reasoning.

©2016 Great Minds. eureka-math.org
G7-M1M2-SE-B1-1.3.1-02.2016

EUREKA
MATH

Lesson 7: Unit Rate as the Constant of Proportionality

Classwork

Example 1: National Forest Deer Population in Danger?

Wildlife conservationists are concerned that the deer population might not be constant across the National Forest. The scientists found that there were 144 deer in a 16-square-mile area of the forest. In another part of the forest, conservationists counted 117 deer in a 13-square-mile area. Yet a third conservationist counted 216 deer in a 24-square-mile plot of the forest. Do conservationists need to be worried?

   a.   Why does it matter if the deer population is not constant in a certain area of the National Forest?

   b.   What is the population density of deer per square mile?

         The unit rate of deer per 1 square mile is _____.

         Constant of Proportionality:

         Explain the meaning of the constant of proportionality in this problem:

   c.   Use the unit rate of deer per square mile (or $\frac{y}{x}$) to determine how many deer there are for every 207 square miles.

   d.   Use the unit rate to determine the number of square miles in which you would find 486 deer.

Vocabulary

A *variable* is a symbol (such as a letter) that is a placeholder for a number.

If a proportional relationship is described by the set of ordered pairs (x, y) that satisfies the equation $y = kx$ for some number k, then k is called the *constant of proportionality*. It is the number that describes the multiplicative relationship between measures, x and y, of two types of quantities. The (x, y) pairs represent all the pairs of numbers that make the equation true.

Note: In a given situation, it would be reasonable to assign any variable as a placeholder for the given measures. For example, a set of ordered pairs (t, d) would be all the points that satisfy the equation $d = rt$, where r is the constant of proportionality. This value for r specifies a number for the given situation.

Example 2: You Need WHAT?

Brandon came home from school and informed his mother that he had volunteered to make cookies for his entire grade level. He needs 3 cookies for each of the 96 students in seventh grade. Unfortunately, he needs the cookies the very next day! Brandon and his mother determined that they can fit 36 cookies on two cookie sheets.

a. Is the number of cookies proportional to the number of cookie sheets used in baking? Create a table that shows data for the number of sheets needed for the total number of cookies baked.

   Table:

   The unit rate of $\dfrac{y}{x}$ is _____.

   Constant of Proportionality:

   Explain the meaning of the constant of proportionality in this problem:

b. It takes 2 hours to bake 8 sheets of cookies. If Brandon and his mother begin baking at 4:00 p.m., when will they finish baking the cookies?

Example 3: French Class Cooking

Suzette and Margo want to prepare crêpes for all of the students in their French class. A recipe makes 20 crêpes with a certain amount of flour, milk, and 2 eggs. The girls already know that they have plenty of flour and milk to make 50 crêpes, but they need to determine the number of eggs they will need for the recipe because they are not sure they have enough.

a. Considering the amount of eggs necessary to make the crêpes, what is the constant of proportionality?

b. What does the constant or proportionality mean in the context of this problem?

c. How many eggs are needed to make 50 crêpes?

Lesson Summary

If a proportional relationship is described by the set of ordered pairs (x, y) that satisfies the equation $y = kx$ for some number k, then k is called the *constant of proportionality*.

Problem Set

For each of the following problems, define the constant of proportionality to answer the follow-up question.

1. Bananas are $0.59/pound.
    a.   What is the constant of proportionality, or k?
    b.   How much will 25 pounds of bananas cost?

2. The dry cleaning fee for 3 pairs of pants is $18.
    a.   What is the constant of proportionality?
    b.   How much will the dry cleaner charge for 11 pairs of pants?

3. For every $5 that Micah saves, his parents give him $10.
    a.   What is the constant of proportionality?
    b.   If Micah saves $150, how much money will his parents give him?

4. Each school year, the seventh graders who study Life Science participate in a special field trip to the city zoo. In 2010, the school paid $1,260 for 84 students to enter the zoo. In 2011, the school paid $1,050 for 70 students to enter the zoo. In 2012, the school paid $1,395 for 93 students to enter the zoo.
    a.   Is the price the school pays each year in entrance fees proportional to the number of students entering the zoo?
    b.   Explain why or why not.
    c.   Identify the constant of proportionality, and explain what it means in the context of this situation.
    d.   What would the school pay if 120 students entered the zoo?
    e.   How many students would enter the zoo if the school paid $1,425?

Lesson 8: Representing Proportional Relationships with Equations

Classwork

Points to remember:

- Proportional relationships have a constant ratio, or unit rate.
- The constant ratio, or unit rate of $\frac{y}{x}$, can also be called the constant of proportionality.

Discussion Notes

How could we use what we know about the constant of proportionality to write an equation?

Example 1: Do We Have Enough Gas to Make It to the Gas Station?

Your mother has accelerated onto the interstate beginning a long road trip, and you notice that the low fuel light is on, indicating that there is a half a gallon left in the gas tank. The nearest gas station is 26 miles away. Your mother keeps a log where she records the mileage and the number of gallons purchased each time she fills up the tank. Use the information in the table below to determine whether you will make it to the gas station before the gas runs out. You know that if you can determine the amount of gas that her car consumes in a particular number of miles, then you can determine whether or not you can make it to the next gas station.

Mother's Gas Record

Gallons	Miles Driven
8	224
10	280
4	112

a. Find the constant of proportionality, and explain what it represents in this situation.

b. Write equation(s) that will relate the miles driven to the number of gallons of gas.

c. Knowing that there is a half gallon left in the gas tank when the light comes on, will she make it to the nearest gas station? Explain why or why not.

d. Using the equation found in part (b), determine how far your mother can travel on 18 gallons of gas. Solve the problem in two ways: once using the constant of proportionality and once using an equation.

e. Using the constant of proportionality, and then using the equation found in part (b), determine how many gallons of gas would be needed to travel 750 miles.

©2016 Great Minds. eureka-math.org
G7-M1M2-SE-B1-1.3.1-02.2016

Example 2: Andrea's Portraits

Andrea is a street artist in New Orleans. She draws caricatures (cartoon-like portraits) of tourists. People have their portrait drawn and then come back later to pick it up from her. The graph below shows the relationship between the number of portraits she draws and the amount of time in hours she needs to draw the portraits.

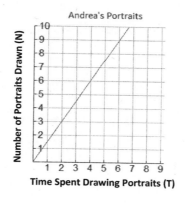

Andrea's Portraits

a. Write several ordered pairs from the graph, and explain what each ordered pair means in the context of this graph.

b. Write several equations that would relate the number of portraits drawn to the time spent drawing the portraits.

c. Determine the constant of proportionality, and explain what it means in this situation.

Lesson Summary

If a proportional relationship is described by the set of ordered pairs that satisfies the equation $y = kx$, where k is a positive constant, then k is called the *constant of proportionality*. The constant of proportionality expresses the multiplicative relationship between each x-value and its corresponding y-value.

Problem Set

Write an equation that will model the proportional relationship given in each real-world situation.

1. There are 3 cans that store 9 tennis balls. Consider the number of balls per can.
   a. Find the constant of proportionality for this situation.
   b. Write an equation to represent the relationship.

2. In 25 minutes Li can run 10 laps around the track. Determine the number of laps she can run per minute.
   a. Find the constant of proportionality in this situation.
   b. Write an equation to represent the relationship.

3. Jennifer is shopping with her mother. They pay $2 per pound for tomatoes at the vegetable stand.
   a. Find the constant of proportionality in this situation.
   b. Write an equation to represent the relationship.

4. It costs $15 to send 3 packages through a certain shipping company. Consider the number of packages per dollar.
   a. Find the constant of proportionality for this situation.
   b. Write an equation to represent the relationship.

5. On average, Susan downloads 60 songs per month. An online music vendor sells package prices for songs that can be downloaded onto personal digital devices. The graph below shows the package prices for the most popular promotions. Susan wants to know if she should buy her music from this company or pay a flat fee of $58.00 per month offered by another company. Which is the better buy?

   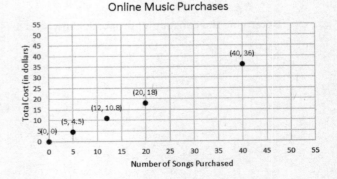

   Online Music Purchases

   a. Find the constant of proportionality for this situation.
   b. Write an equation to represent the relationship.
   c. Use your equation to find the answer to Susan's question above. Justify your answer with mathematical evidence and a written explanation.

Lesson 8:   Representing Proportional Relationships with Equations

EUREKA MATH™

©2016 Great Minds. eureka-math.org
G7-M1M2-SE-B1-1.3.1-02.2016

6. Allison's middle school team has designed t-shirts containing their team name and color. Allison and her friend
    Nicole have volunteered to call local stores to get an estimate on the total cost of purchasing t-shirts. Print-o-Rama
    charges a set-up fee, as well as a fixed amount for each shirt ordered. The total cost is shown below for the given
    number of shirts. Value T's and More charges $8 per shirt. Which company should they use?

Print-o-Rama

Number of Shirts (S)	Total Cost (C)
10	95
25	
50	375
75	
100	

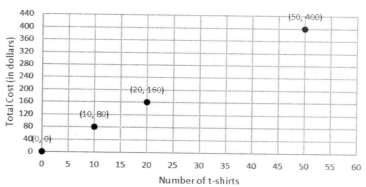

Value T's and More

a. Does either pricing model represent a proportional relationship between the quantity of t-shirts and the total
    cost? Explain.

b. Write an equation relating cost and shirts for Value T's and More.

c. What is the constant of proportionality of Value T's and More? What does it represent?

d. How much is Print-o-Rama's set-up fee?

e. If you need to purchase 90 shirts, write a proposal to your teacher indicating which company the team should
    use. Be sure to support your choice. Determine the number of shirts that you need for your team.

This page intentionally left blank

Lesson 9: Representing Proportional Relationships with Equations

Classwork

Example 1: Jackson's Birdhouses

Jackson and his grandfather constructed a model for a birdhouse. Many of their neighbors offered to buy the birdhouses. Jackson decided that building birdhouses could help him earn money for his summer camp, but he is not sure how long it will take him to finish all of the requests for birdhouses. If Jackson can build 7 birdhouses in 5 hours, write an equation that will allow Jackson to calculate the time it will take him to build any given number of birdhouses, assuming he works at a constant rate.

 a.   Write an equation that you could use to find out how long it will take him to build any number of birdhouses.

 b.   How many birdhouses can Jackson build in 40 hours?

 c.   How long will it take Jackson to build 35 birdhouses? Use the equation from part (a) to solve the problem.

 d.   How long will it take to build 71 birdhouses? Use the equation from part (a) to solve the problem.

Example 2: Al's Produce Stand

Al's Produce Stand sells 6 ears of corn for $1.50. Barbara's Produce Stand sells 13 ears of corn for $3.12. Write two equations, one for each produce stand, that model the relationship between the number of ears of corn sold and the cost. Then, use each equation to help complete the tables below.

Al's Produce Stand   Barbara's Produce Stand

Ears	6	14	21		Ears	13	14	21	
Cost	$1.50			$50.00	Cost	$3.12			$49.92

EUREKA MATH

©2016 Great Minds. eureka-math.org
G7-M1M2-SE-B1-1.3.1-02.2016

Lesson Summary

How do you find the constant of proportionality? Divide to find the unit rate, $\frac{y}{x} = k$.

How do you write an equation for a proportional relationship? $y = kx$, substituting the value of the constant of proportionality in place of k.

What is the structure of proportional relationship equations, and how do we use them? x and y values are always left as variables, and when one of them is known, they are substituted into $y = kx$ to find the unknown using algebra.

Problem Set

1. A person who weighs 100 pounds on Earth weighs 16.6 lb. on the moon.

    a. Which variable is the independent variable? Explain why.

    b. What is an equation that relates weight on Earth to weight on the moon?

    c. How much would a 185-pound astronaut weigh on the moon? Use an equation to explain how you know.

    d. How much would a man who weighs 50 pounds on the moon weigh on Earth?

2. Use this table to answer the following questions.

Number of Gallons of Gas	Number of Miles Driven
0	0
2	62
4	124
10	310

    a. Which variable is the dependent variable, and why?

    b. Is the number of miles driven proportionally related to the number of gallons of gas consumed? If so, what is the equation that relates the number of miles driven to the number of gallons of gas?

    c. In any ratio relating the number of gallons of gas and the number of miles driven, will one of the values always be larger? If so, which one?

    d. If the number of gallons of gas is known, can you find the number of miles driven? Explain how this value would be calculated.

    e. If the number of miles driven is known, can you find the number of gallons of gas consumed? Explain how this value would be calculated.

    f. How many miles could be driven with 18 gallons of gas?

    g. How many gallons are used when the car has been driven 18 miles?

    h. How many miles have been driven when half a gallon of gas is used?

    i. How many gallons of gas have been used when the car has been driven for a half mile?

3. Suppose that the cost of renting a snowmobile is $37.50 for 5 hours.

    a. If c represents the cost and h represents the hours, which variable is the dependent variable? Explain why.

    b. What would be the cost of renting 2 snowmobiles for 5 hours?

4. In Katya's car, the number of miles driven is proportional to the number of gallons of gas used. Find the missing value in the table.

Number of Gallons	Number of Miles Driven
0	0
4	112
6	168
	224
10	280

    a. Write an equation that will relate the number of miles driven to the number of gallons of gas.

    b. What is the constant of proportionality?

    c. How many miles could Katya go if she filled her 22-gallon tank?

    d. If Katya takes a trip of 600 miles, how many gallons of gas would be needed to make the trip?

    e. If Katya drives 224 miles during one week of commuting to school and work, how many gallons of gas would she use?

EUREKA
MATH

Lesson 10: Interpreting Graphs of Proportional Relationships

Classwork

Example 1

Grandma's special chocolate chip cookie recipe, which yields 4 dozen cookies, calls for 3 cups of flour.

Using this information, complete the chart:

Create a table comparing the amount of flour used to the amount of cookies.	Is the number of cookies proportional to the amount of flour used? Explain why or why not.	What is the unit rate of cookies to flour $\left(\frac{y}{x}\right)$, and what is the meaning in the context of the problem?
Model the relationship on a graph. 	Does the graph show the two quantities being proportional to each other? Explain.	Write an equation that can be used to represent the relationship.

Example 2

Below is a graph modeling the amount of sugar required to make Grandma's special chocolate chip cookies.

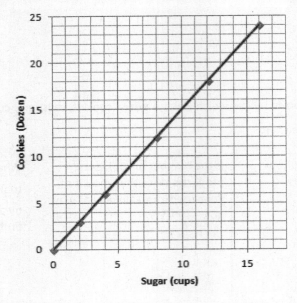

a. Record the coordinates from the graph. What do these ordered pairs represent?

b. Grandma has 1 remaining cup of sugar. How many dozen cookies will she be able to make? Plot the point on the graph above.

c. How many dozen cookies can Grandma make if she has no sugar? Can you graph this on the coordinate plane provided above? What do we call this point?

©2016 Great Minds. eureka-math.org
G7-M1M2-SE-B1-1.3.1-02.2016

EUREKA
MATH

Exercises

1. The graph below shows the amount of time a person can shower with a certain amount of water.

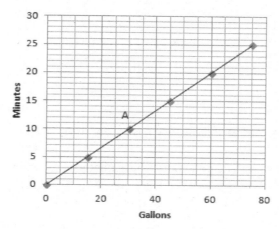

a. Can you determine by looking at the graph whether the length of the shower is proportional to the number of gallons of water? Explain how you know.

b. How long can a person shower with 15 gallons of water? How long can a person shower with 60 gallons of water?

c. What are the coordinates of point A? Describe point A in the context of the problem.

d. Can you use the graph to identify the unit rate?

e. Write the equation to represent the relationship between the number of gallons of water used and the length of a shower.

2. Your friend uses the equation $C = 50P$ to find the total cost, C, for the number of people, P, entering a local amusement park.

a. Create a table and record the cost of entering the amusement park for several different-sized groups of people.

b. Is the cost of admission proportional to the amount of people entering the amusement park? Explain why or why not.

c. What is the unit rate, and what does it represent in the context of the situation?

EUREKA
MATH™

©2016 Great Minds. eureka-math.org
G7-M1M2-SE-B1-1.3.1-02.2016

d.   Sketch a graph to represent this relationship.

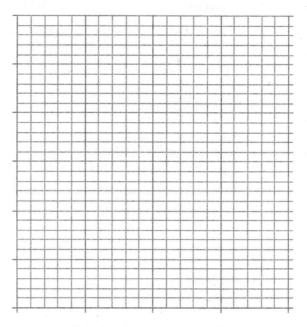

e.   What points must be on the graph of the line if the two quantities represented are proportional to each other? Explain why, and describe these points in the context of the problem.

f.   Would the point (5, 250) be on the graph? What does this point represent in the context of the situation?

Lesson Summary

The points $(0, 0)$ and $(1, r)$, where r is the unit rate, will always appear on the line representing two quantities that are proportional to each other.

- The unit rate, r, in the point $(1, r)$ represents the amount of vertical increase for every horizontal increase of 1 unit on the graph.

- The point $(0, 0)$ indicates that when there is zero amount of one quantity, there will also be zero amount of the second quantity.

These two points may not always be given as part of the set of data for a given real-world or mathematical situation, but they will always appear on the line that passes through the given data points.

Problem Set

1. The graph to the right shows the relationship of the amount of time (in seconds) to the distance (in feet) run by a jaguar.

    a. What does the point $(5, 290)$ represent in the context of the situation?

    b. What does the point $(3, 174)$ represent in the context of the situation?

    c. Is the distance run by the jaguar proportional to the time? Explain why or why not.

    d. Write an equation to represent the distance run by the jaguar. Explain or model your reasoning.

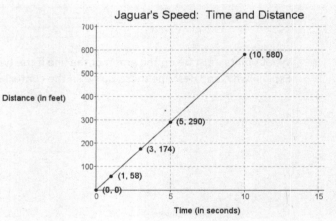

2. Championship t-shirts sell for $22 each.

    a. What point(s) must be on the graph for the quantities to be proportional to each other?

    b. What does the ordered pair $(5, 110)$ represent in the context of this problem?

    c. How many t-shirts were sold if you spent a total of $88?

3. The graph represents the total cost of renting a car. The cost of renting a car is a fixed amount each day, regardless of how many miles the car is driven.

    a. What does the ordered pair $(4, 250)$ represent?

    b. What would be the cost to rent the car for a week? Explain or model your reasoning.

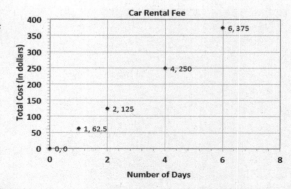

©2016 Great Minds. eureka-math.org
G7-M1M2-SE-B1-1.3.1-02.2016

4. Jackie is making a snack mix for a party. She is using cashews and peanuts. The table below shows the relationship of the number of packages of cashews she needs to the number of cans of peanuts she needs to make the mix.

Packages of Cashews	Cans of Peanuts
0	0
1	2
2	4
3	6
4	8

a. Write an equation to represent this relationship.

b. Describe the ordered pair $(12, 24)$ in the context of the problem.

5. The following table shows the amount of candy and price paid.

Amount of Candy (in pounds)	2	3	5
Cost (in dollars)	5	7.5	12.5

a. Is the cost of the candy proportional to the amount of candy?

b. Write an equation to illustrate the relationship between the amount of candy and the cost.

c. Using the equation, predict how much it will cost for 12 pounds of candy.

d. What is the maximum amount of candy you can buy with $60?

e. Graph the relationship.

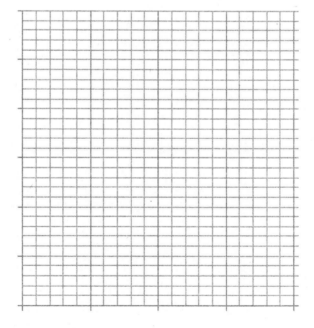

This page intentionally left blank

Lesson 11: Ratios of Fractions and Their Unit Rates

Example 1: Who is Faster?

During their last workout, Izzy ran $2\frac{1}{4}$ miles in 15 minutes, and her friend Julia ran $3\frac{3}{4}$ miles in 25 minutes. Each girl thought she was the faster runner. Based on their last run, which girl is correct? Use any approach to find the solution.

©2016 Great Minds. eureka-math.org
G7-M1M2-SE-B1-1.3.1-02.2016

Example 2: Is Meredith Correct?

A turtle walks $\frac{7}{8}$ of a mile in 50 minutes. What is the unit rate when the turtle's speed is expressed in miles per hour?

a. To find the turtle's unit rate, Meredith wrote the following complex fraction. Explain how the fraction $\frac{5}{6}$ was obtained.

$$\frac{\left(\frac{7}{8}\right)}{\left(\frac{5}{6}\right)}$$

b. Determine the unit rate when the turtle's speed is expressed in miles per hour.

Exercises

1. For Anthony's birthday, his mother is making cupcakes for his 12 friends at his daycare. The recipe calls for $3\frac{1}{3}$ cups of flour. This recipe makes $2\frac{1}{2}$ dozen cupcakes. Anthony's mother has only 1 cup of flour. Is there enough flour for each of his friends to get a cupcake? Explain and show your work.

2. Sally is making a painting for which she is mixing red paint and blue paint. The table below shows the different mixtures being used.

Red Paint (Quarts)	Blue Paint (Quarts)
$1\frac{1}{2}$	$2\frac{1}{2}$
$2\frac{2}{5}$	4
$3\frac{3}{4}$	$6\frac{1}{4}$
4	$6\frac{2}{3}$
1.2	2
1.8	3

a. What is the unit rate for the values of the amount of blue paint to the amount of red paint?

b. Is the amount of blue paint proportional to the amount of red paint?

c. Describe, in words, what the unit rate means in the context of this problem.

Lesson Summary

A number written in fraction form whose numerator or denominator is itself a fraction is called a *complex fraction*.

If a proportional relationship is given by a description such as, "A person walks $2\frac{1}{2}$ miles in $1\frac{1}{4}$ hours at a constant speed," then the unit rate is

$$\frac{2\frac{1}{2}}{1\frac{1}{4}} = \frac{\frac{5}{2}}{\frac{5}{4}} = \frac{5}{2} \cdot \frac{4}{5} = 2. \text{ The person walks 2 mph.}$$

Problem Set

1. Determine the quotient: $2\frac{4}{7} \div 1\frac{3}{6}$.

2. One lap around a dirt track is $\frac{1}{3}$ mile. It takes Bryce $\frac{1}{9}$ hour to ride one lap. What is Bryce's unit rate, in miles, around the track?

3. Mr. Gengel wants to make a shelf with boards that are $1\frac{1}{3}$ feet long. If he has an 18-foot board, how many pieces can he cut from the big board?

4. The local bakery uses 1.75 cups of flour in each batch of cookies. The bakery used 5.25 cups of flour this morning.
   a. How many batches of cookies did the bakery make?
   b. If there are 5 dozen cookies in each batch, how many cookies did the bakery make?

5. Jason eats 10 ounces of candy in 5 days.
   a. How many <u>pounds</u> does he eat per day? (Recall: 16 ounces = 1 pound)
   b. How long will it take Jason to eat 1 pound of candy?

EUREKA MATH

Lesson 12: Ratios of Fractions and Their Unit Rates

Classwork

During this lesson, you are remodeling a room at your house and need to figure out if you have enough money. You will work individually and with a partner to make a plan of what is needed to solve the problem. After your plan is complete, then you will solve the problem by determining if you have enough money.

Example 1: Time to Remodel

You have decided to remodel your bathroom and install a tile floor. The bathroom is in the shape of a rectangle, and the floor measures 14 feet, 8 inches long by 5 feet, 6 inches wide. The tiles you want to use cost $5 each, and each tile covers $4\frac{2}{3}$ square feet. If you have $100 to spend, do you have enough money to complete the project?

Make a Plan: Complete the chart to identify the necessary steps in the plan and find a solution.

What I Know	What I Want to Find	How to Find it

Compare your plan with a partner. Using your plans, work together to determine how much money you will need to complete the project and if you have enough money.

Exercise

Which car can travel farther on 1 gallon of gas?

Blue Car: travels $18\frac{2}{5}$ miles using 0.8 gallons of gas

Red Car: travels $17\frac{2}{5}$ miles using 0.75 gallons of gas

Problem Set

1. You are getting ready for a family vacation. You decide to download as many movies as possible before leaving for the road trip. If each movie takes $1\frac{2}{5}$ hours to download, and you downloaded for $5\frac{1}{4}$ hours, how many movies did you download?

2. The area of a blackboard is $1\frac{1}{3}$ square yards. A poster's area is $\frac{8}{9}$ square yards. Find the unit rate and explain, in words, what the unit rate means in the context of this problem. Is there more than one unit rate that can be calculated? How do you know?

3. A toy jeep is $12\frac{1}{2}$ inches long, while an actual jeep measures $18\frac{3}{4}$ feet long. What is the value of the ratio of the length of the toy jeep to the length of the actual jeep? What does the ratio mean in this situation?

4. To make 5 dinner rolls, $\frac{1}{3}$ cup of flour is used.

   a. How much flour is needed to make one dinner roll?

   b. How many cups of flour are needed to make 3 dozen dinner rolls?

   c. How many rolls can you make with $5\frac{2}{3}$ cups of flour?

This page intentionally left blank

Lesson 13: Finding Equivalent Ratios Given the Total Quantity

Classwork

Example 1

A group of 6 hikers are preparing for a one-week trip. All of the group's supplies will be carried by the hikers in backpacks. The leader decides that each hiker will carry a backpack that is the same fraction of weight to all the other hikers' weights. This means that the heaviest hiker would carry the heaviest load. The table below shows the weight of each hiker and the weight of the backpack.

Complete the table. Find the missing amounts of weight by applying the same value of the ratio as the first two rows.

Hiker's Weight	Backpack Weight	Total Weight (lb.)
152 lb. 4 oz.	14 lb. 8 oz.	
107 lb. 10 oz.	10 lb. 4 oz.	
129 lb. 15 oz.		
68 lb. 4 oz.		
	8 lb. 12 oz.	
	10 lb.	

Example 2

When a business buys a fast food franchise, it is buying the recipes used at every restaurant with the same name. For example, all Pizzeria Specialty House Restaurants have different owners, but they must all use the same recipes for their pizza, sauce, bread, etc. You are now working at your local Pizzeria Specialty House Restaurant, and listed below are the amounts of meat used on one meat-lovers pizza.

$\frac{1}{4}$ cup of sausage

$\frac{1}{3}$ cup of pepperoni

$\frac{1}{6}$ cup of bacon

$\frac{1}{8}$ cup of ham

$\frac{1}{8}$ cup of beef

What is the total amount of toppings used on a meat-lovers pizza? _____ cup(s)

The meat must be mixed using this ratio to ensure that customers receive the same great tasting meat-lovers pizza from every Pizzeria Specialty House Restaurant nationwide. The table below shows 3 different orders for meat-lovers pizzas on the night of the professional football championship game. Using the amounts and total for one pizza given above, fill in every row and column of the table so the mixture tastes the same.

	Order 1	Order 2	Order 3
Sausage (cups)	1		
Pepperoni (cups)			3
Bacon (cups)		1	
Ham (cups)	$\frac{1}{2}$		
Beef (cups)			$1\frac{1}{8}$
TOTAL (cups)			

EUREKA
MATH™

Exercise

The table below shows 6 different-sized pans that could be used to make macaroni and cheese. If the ratio of ingredients stays the same, how might the recipe be altered to account for the different-sized pans?

Noodles (cups)	Cheese (cups)	Pan Size (cups)
		5
3	$\frac{3}{4}$	
	$\frac{1}{4}$	
$\frac{2}{3}$		
$5\frac{1}{3}$		
		$5\frac{5}{8}$

Lesson Summary

To find missing quantities in a ratio table where a total is given, determine the unit rate from the ratio of two given quantities, and use it to find the missing quantities in each equivalent ratio.

Problem Set

1. Students in 6 classes, displayed below, ate the same ratio of cheese pizza slices to pepperoni pizza slices. Complete the following table, which represents the number of slices of pizza students in each class ate.

Slices of Cheese Pizza	Slices of Pepperoni Pizza	Total Slices of Pizza
		7
6	15	
8		
	$13\frac{3}{4}$	
$3\frac{1}{3}$		
		$2\frac{1}{10}$

2. To make green paint, students mixed yellow paint with blue paint. The table below shows how many yellow and blue drops from a dropper several students used to make the same shade of green paint.

   a. Complete the table.

Yellow (Y) (mL)	Blue (B) (mL)	Total (mL)
$3\frac{1}{2}$	$5\frac{1}{4}$	
		5
	$6\frac{3}{4}$	
$6\frac{1}{2}$		

   b. Write an equation to represent the relationship between the amount of yellow paint and blue paint.

3. The ratio of the number of miles run to the number of miles biked is equivalent for each row in the table.

   a. Complete the table.

Distance Run (miles)	Distance Biked (miles)	Total Amount of Exercise (miles)
		6
$3\frac{1}{2}$	7	
	$5\frac{1}{2}$	
$2\frac{1}{8}$		
	$3\frac{1}{3}$	

   b. What is the relationship between distances biked and distances run?

4. The following table shows the number of cups of milk and flour that are needed to make biscuits. Complete the table.

Milk (cups)	Flour (cups)	Total (cups)
7.5		
	10.5	
12.5	15	
		11

This page intentionally left blank

Lesson 14: Multi-Step Ratio Problems

Classwork

Example 1: Bargains

Peter's Pants Palace advertises the following sale: Shirts are $\frac{1}{2}$ off the original price; pants are $\frac{1}{3}$ off the original price; and shoes are $\frac{1}{4}$ off the original price.

    a.   If a pair of shoes costs $40, what is the sales price?

    b.   At Peter's Pants Palace, a pair of pants usually sells for $33.00. What is the sale price of Peter's pants?

Example 2: Big Al's Used Cars

A used car salesperson receives a commission of $\frac{1}{12}$ of the sales price of the car for each car he sells. What would the sales commission be on a car that sold for $21,999?

Example 3: Tax Time

As part of a marketing plan, some businesses mark up their prices before they advertise a sales event. Some companies use this practice as a way to entice customers into the store without sacrificing their profits.

A furniture store wants to host a sales event to improve its profit margin and to reduce its tax liability before its inventory is taxed at the end of the year.

How much profit will the business make on the sale of a couch that is marked up by $\frac{1}{3}$ and then sold at a $\frac{1}{5}$ off discount if the original price is $2,400?

Example 4: Born to Ride

A motorcycle dealer paid a certain price for a motorcycle and marked it up by $\frac{1}{5}$ of the price he paid. Later, he sold it for $14,000. What was the original price?

©2016 Great Minds. eureka-math.org
G7-M1M2-SE-B1-1.3.1-02.2016

Problem Set

1. A salesperson will earn a commission equal to $\frac{1}{32}$ of the total sales. What is the commission earned on sales totaling $24,000?

2. DeMarkus says that a store overcharged him on the price of the video game he bought. He thought that the price was marked $\frac{1}{4}$ of the original price, but it was really $\frac{1}{4}$ off the original price. He misread the advertisement. If the original price of the game was $48, what is the difference between the price that DeMarkus thought he should pay and the price that the store charged him?

3. What is the cost of a $1,200 washing machine after a discount of $\frac{1}{5}$ the original price?

4. If a store advertised a sale that gave customers a $\frac{1}{4}$ discount, what is the fractional part of the original price that the customer will pay?

5. Mark bought an electronic tablet on sale for $\frac{1}{4}$ off the original price of $825.00. He also wanted to use a coupon for $\frac{1}{5}$ off the sales price. How much did Mark pay for the tablet?

6. A car dealer paid a certain price for a car and marked it up by $\frac{7}{5}$ of the price he paid. Later, he sold it for $24,000. What is the original price?

7. Joanna ran a mile in physical education class. After resting for one hour, her heart rate was 60 beats per minute. If her heart rate decreased by $\frac{2}{5}$, what was her heart rate immediately after she ran the mile?

This page intentionally left blank

Lesson 15: Equations of Graphs of Proportional Relationships Involving Fractions

Classwork

Example 1: Mother's 10K Race

Sam's mother has entered a 10K race. Sam and his family want to show their support of their mother, but they need to figure out where they should go along the race course. They also need to determine how long it will take her to run the race so that they will know when to meet her at the finish line. Previously, his mother ran a 5K race with a time of $1\frac{1}{2}$ hours. Assume Sam's mother ran the same rate as the previous race in order to complete the chart.

Create a table that shows how far Sam's mother has run after each half hour from the start of the race, and graph it on the coordinate plane to the right.

Time (H, in hours)	Distance Run (D, in kilometers)

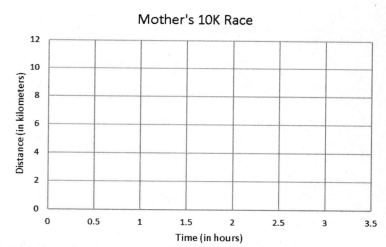

Mother's 10K Race

a. What are some specific things you notice about this graph?

b. What is the connection between the table and the graph?

c. What does the ordered pair $\left(2, 6\frac{2}{3}\right)$ represent in the context of this problem?

©2016 Great Minds. eureka-math.org
G7-M1M2-SE-B1-1.3.1-02.2016

Example 2: Gourmet Cooking

After taking a cooking class, you decide to try out your new cooking skills by preparing a meal for your family. You have chosen a recipe that uses gourmet mushrooms as the main ingredient. Using the graph below, complete the table of values and answer the following questions.

Weight (in pounds)	Cost (in dollars)
0	0
$\frac{1}{2}$	4
1	
$1\frac{1}{2}$	12
	16
$2\frac{1}{4}$	18

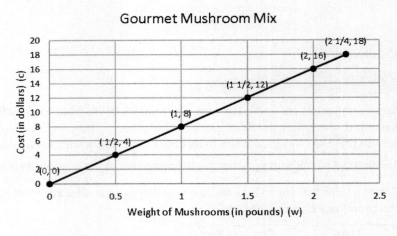

Gourmet Mushroom Mix

a.   Is this relationship proportional? How do you know from examining the graph?

b.   What is the unit rate for cost per pound?

c.   Write an equation to model this data.

d.   What ordered pair represents the unit rate, and what does it mean?

e.   What does the ordered pair $(2, 16)$ mean in the context of this problem?

f.   If you could spend $10.00 on mushrooms, how many pounds could you buy?

g.   What would be the cost of 30 pounds of mushrooms?

EUREKA
MATH™

Lesson Summary

Proportional relationships can be represented through the use of graphs, tables, equations, diagrams, and verbal descriptions.

In a proportional relationship arising from ratios and rates involving fractions, *the graph* gives a visual display of *all values* of the proportional relationship, especially the quantities that fall between integer values.

Problem Set

1. Students are responsible for providing snacks and drinks for the Junior Beta Club Induction Reception. Susan and Myra were asked to provide the punch for the 100 students and family members who will attend the event. The chart below will help Susan and Myra determine the proportion of cranberry juice to sparkling water needed to make the punch. Complete the chart, graph the data, and write the equation that models this proportional relationship.

Sparkling Water (S, in cups)	Cranberry Juice (C, in cups)
1	$\dfrac{4}{5}$
5	4
8	
12	$9\dfrac{3}{5}$
	40
100	

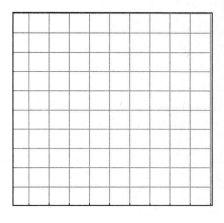

2. Jenny is a member of a summer swim team.

    a. Using the graph, determine how many calories she burns in one minute.

    b. Use the graph to determine the equation that models the number of calories Jenny burns within a certain number of minutes.

    c. How long will it take her to burn off a 480-calorie smoothie that she had for breakfast?

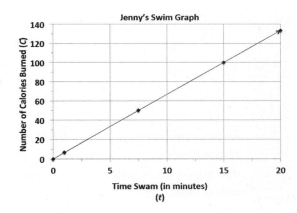

Jenny's Swim Graph

Number of Calories Burned (C)

Time Swam (in minutes) (t)

3. Students in a world geography class want to determine the distances between cities in Europe. The map gives all distances in kilometers. The students want to determine the number of miles between towns so that they can compare distances with a unit of measure with which they are already familiar. The graph below shows the relationship between a given number of kilometers and the corresponding number of miles.

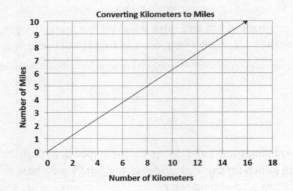

a. Find the constant of proportionality, or the rate of miles per kilometer, for this problem, and write the equation that models this relationship.

b. What is the distance in kilometers between towns that are 5 miles apart?

c. Describe the steps you would take to determine the distance in miles between two towns that are 200 kilometers apart?

4. During summer vacation, Lydie spent time with her grandmother picking blackberries. They decided to make blackberry jam for their family. Her grandmother said that you must cook the berries until they become juice and then combine the juice with the other ingredients to make the jam.

a. Use the table below to determine the constant of proportionality of cups of juice to cups of blackberries.

Cups of Blackberries	Cups of Juice
0	0
4	$1\frac{1}{3}$
8	$2\frac{2}{3}$
12	
	8

b. Write an equation that models the relationship between the number of cups of blackberries and the number of cups of juice.

c. How many cups of juice were made from 12 cups of berries? How many cups of berries are needed to make 8 cups of juice?

Lesson 16: Relating Scale Drawings to Ratios and Rates

Classwork

Opening Exercise: Can You Guess the Image?

1.

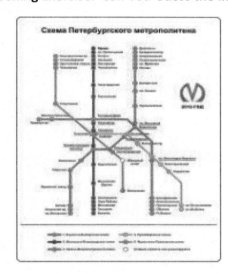

2.

Example 1

For the following problems, (a) is the actual picture, and (b) is the drawing. Is the drawing an enlargement or a reduction of the actual picture?

1. a.   b.

2. a.
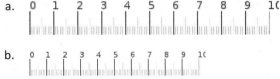

   b.

> **SCALE DRAWING**: A reduced or enlarged two-dimensional drawing of an original two-dimensional drawing.

Example 2

Derek's family took a day trip to a modern public garden. Derek looked at his map of the park that was a reduction of the map located at the garden entrance. The dots represent the placement of rare plants. The diagram below is the top-view as Derek held his map while looking at the posted map.

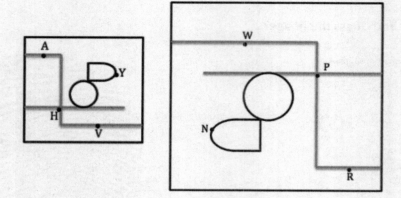

What are the corresponding points of the scale drawings of the maps?

Point A to _____   Point V to _____   Point H to _____   Point Y to _____

©2016 Great Minds. eureka-math.org
G7-M1M2-SE-B1-1.3.1-02.2016

Exploratory Challenge

Create scale drawings of your own modern nesting robots using the grids provided.

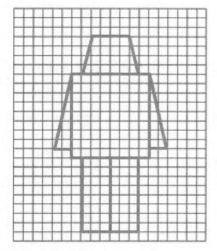

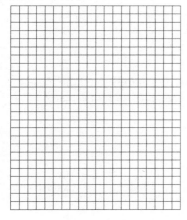

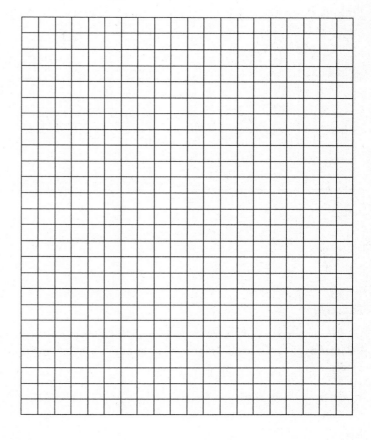

Example 3

Celeste drew an outline of a building for a diagram she was making and then drew a second one mimicking her original drawing. State the coordinates of the vertices and fill in the table.

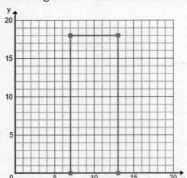
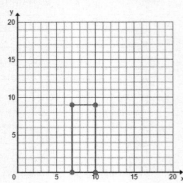

	Height	Length
Original Drawing		
Second Drawing		

Notes:

Exercise

Luca drew and cut out a small right triangle for a mosaic piece he was creating for art class. His mother liked the mosaic piece and asked if he could create a larger one for their living room. Luca made a second template for his triangle pieces.

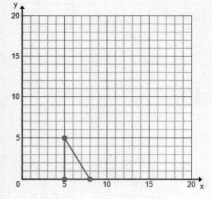
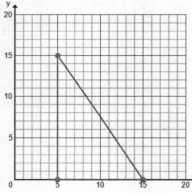

	Height	Width
Original Image		
Second Image		

a.   Fill in the table. Does a constant of proportionality exist? If so, what is it? If not, explain.

b.   Is Luca's enlarged mosaic a scale drawing of the first image? Explain why or why not.

Lesson Summary

SCALE DRAWING AND SCALE FACTOR: For two figures in the plane, S and S', S' is said to be a *scale drawing* of S with *scale factor* r if there is a one-to-one correspondence between S and S' so that, under the pairing of this one-to-one correspondence, the distance $|PQ|$ between any two points P and Q of S is related to the distance $|P'Q'|$ between corresponding points P' and Q' of S' by $|P'Q'| = r|PQ|$.

A scale drawing is an *enlargement* or *magnification* of another figure if the scale drawing is larger than the original drawing, that is, if $r > 1$.

A scale drawing is a *reduction* of another figure if the scale drawing is smaller than the original drawing, that is, if $0 < r < 1$.

Problem Set

For Problems 1–3, identify if the scale drawing is a reduction or an enlargement of the actual picture.

1. _____

    a.   Actual Picture   b.   Scale Drawing

2. _____

   a. Actual Picture

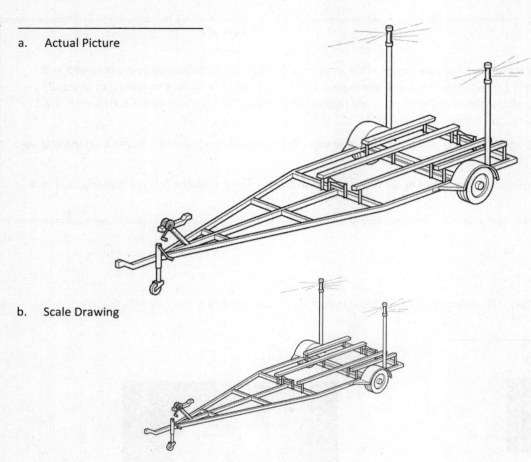

   b. Scale Drawing

3. _____

   a. Actual Picture   b. Scale Drawing

EUREKA
MATH™

4.   Using the grid and the abstract picture of a face, answer the following questions:

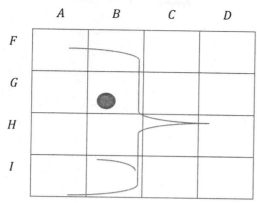

a.   On the grid, where is the eye?

b.   What is located in DH?

c.   In what part of the square BI is the chin located?

5.   Use the blank graph provided to plot the points and decide if the rectangular cakes are scale drawings of each other.
    Cake 1: $(5,3)$, $(5,5)$, $(11,3)$, $(11,5)$
    Cake 2: $(1,6)$, $(1,12)$, $(13,12)$, $(13,6)$
    How do you know?

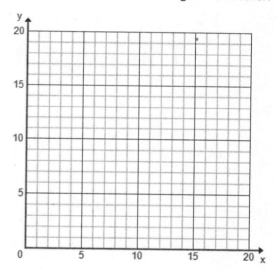

©2016 Great Minds. eureka-math.org
G7-M1M2-SE-B1-1.3.1-02.2016

This page intentionally left blank

Lesson 17: The Unit Rate as the Scale Factor

Classwork

Example 1: Jake's Icon

Jake created a simple game on his computer and shared it with his friends to play. They were instantly hooked, and the popularity of his game spread so quickly that Jake wanted to create a distinctive icon so that players could easily identify his game. He drew a simple sketch. From the sketch, he created stickers to promote his game, but Jake wasn't quite sure if the stickers were proportional to his original sketch.

Original Sketch:

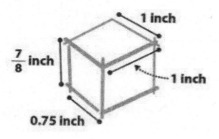

Sticker:

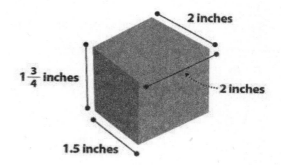

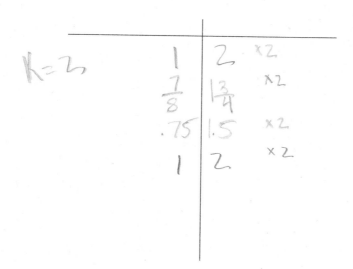

Steps to check for proportionality for scale drawing and original object or picture:

1. Record the lenths of the scale of the table

2. Record the corresponding on the table

3. Check for the constant of Proptailitity (K=)

Key Idea:

The *scale factor* can be calculated from the ratio of any length in the scale drawing to its corresponding length in the actual picture. The scale factor corresponds to the unit rate and the constant of proportionality.

Scaling by factors *greater than* 1 enlarges the segment, and scaling by factors *less than* 1 reduces the segment.

Exercise 1: App Icon

Reduction
K = ½

no high
↓

$\frac{1}{2}$ inch

$\frac{7}{16}$ inch

$\frac{1}{2}$ inch

$1\frac{3}{4}$

$\frac{3}{8}$ inch

.75

1	$\frac{1}{2}$
$1\frac{3}{4}$	$\frac{7}{16}$
.75	$\frac{3}{8}$
1	1

← Not Proptailitity

$$\frac{7}{4} \times \frac{1}{2} = \frac{7}{8}$$

$$\frac{75}{100} = \frac{3}{4} \times \frac{1}{2} = \frac{3}{8}$$

Example 2

Use a Scale Factor of 3 to create a scale drawing of the picture below.

Picture of the flag of Colombia:

Enlargement

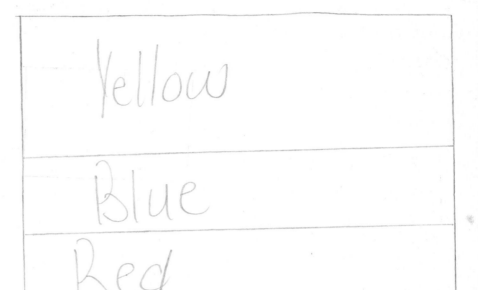

A. $1\frac{1}{2}$
B. $\frac{1}{2}$
C. $\frac{1}{4}$
D. $\frac{1}{4}$

Exercise 2

Scale Factor $= \frac{1}{2}$

Sketch and notes:

Picture of the flag of Colombia:

Reduction

Example 3

Your family recently had a family portrait taken. Your aunt asks you to take a picture of the portrait using your phone and send it to her. If the original portrait is 3 feet by 3 feet, and the scale factor is $\frac{1}{18}$, draw the scale drawing that would be the size of the portrait on your phone.

Sketch and notes:

$$x \ \frac{36}{1} \ x \ \frac{1}{18} = \frac{36}{18} = 2$$

2

2"

2

2

Exercise 3

John is building his daughter a doll house that is a miniature model of their house. The front of their house has a circular window with a diameter of 5 feet. If the scale factor for the model house is $\frac{1}{30}$, make a sketch of the circular doll house window.

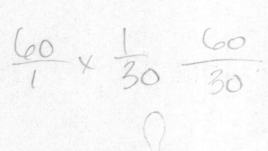

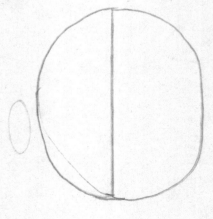

$$\frac{60}{1} \ x \ \frac{1}{30} \quad \frac{60}{30}$$

EUREKA
MATH™

Lesson 18: Computing Actual Lengths from a Scale Drawing

Classwork

Example 1: Basketball at Recess?

Vincent proposes an idea to the Student Government to install a basketball hoop along with a court marked with all the shooting lines and boundary lines at his school for students to use at recess. He presents a plan to install a half-court design as shown below. After checking with the school administration, he is told it will be approved if it fits on the empty lot that measures 25 feet by 75 feet on the school property. Will the lot be big enough for the court he planned? Explain.

Scale Drawing: 1 inch on the drawing corresponds to 15 feet of actual length.

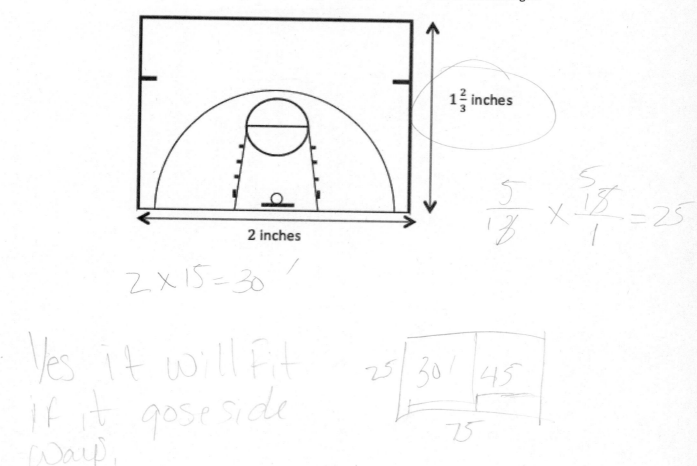

$1\frac{2}{3}$ inches

2 inches

$$\frac{5}{18} \times \frac{18}{1} = 25$$

$$2 \times 15 = 30$$

Yes it will fit
if it goes side
way.

25 | 30' | 45
75

Example 2

The diagram shown represents a garden. The scale is 1 centimeter for every 20 meters. Each square in the drawing measures 1 cm by 1 cm. Find the actual length and width of the garden based upon the given drawing.

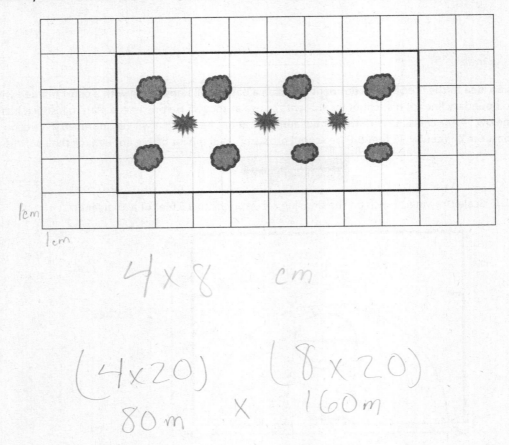

$4 \times 8 \quad cm$

$(4 \times 20) \quad (8 \times 20)$

$80m \quad \times \quad 160m$

EUREKA
MATH™

©2016 Great Minds. eureka-math.org
G7-M1M2-SE-B1-1.3.1-02.2016

Example 3

A graphic designer is creating an advertisement for a tablet. She needs to enlarge the picture given here so that 0.25 inches on the scale picture corresponds to 1 inch on the actual advertisement. What will be the length and width of the tablet on the advertisement?

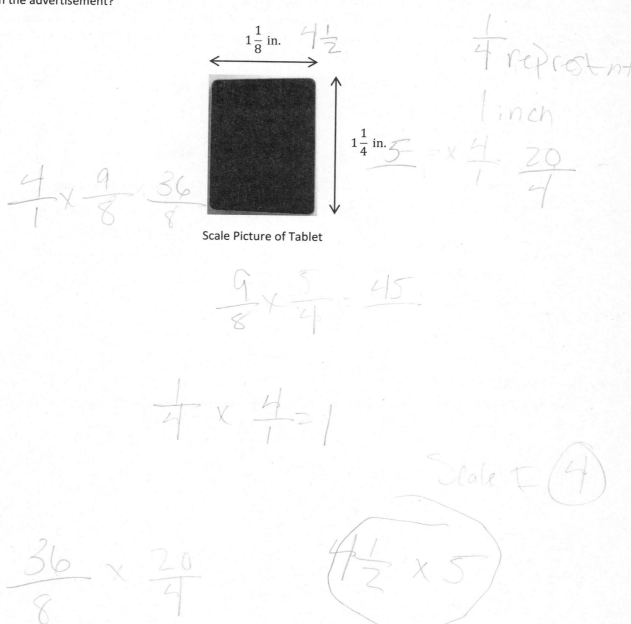

$1\frac{1}{8}$ in. $4\frac{1}{2}$

$1\frac{1}{4}$ in.

Scale Picture of Tablet

$\frac{1}{4}$ represent 1 inch

$5 = x \cdot \frac{4}{1} \quad \frac{20}{4}$

$\frac{4}{1} \times \frac{9}{8} = \frac{36}{8}$

$\frac{9}{8} \times \frac{5}{4} = 45$

$\frac{1}{4} \times \frac{4}{1} = 1$

Scale = ④

$\frac{36}{8} \times \frac{20}{4}$

$4\frac{1}{2} \times 5$

Exercise

Students from the high school are going to perform one of the acts from their upcoming musical at the atrium in the mall. The students want to bring some of the set with them so that the audience can get a better feel for the whole production. The backdrop that they want to bring has panels that measure 10 feet by 10 feet. The students are not sure if they will be able to fit these panels through the entrance of the mall since the panels need to be transported flat (horizontal). They obtain a copy of the mall floor plan, shown below, from the city planning office. Use this diagram to decide if the panels will fit through the entrance. Use a ruler to measure.

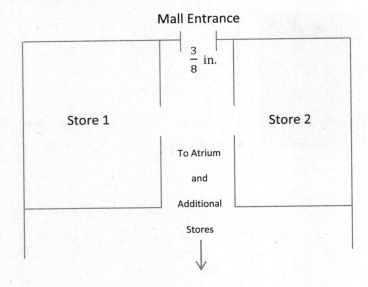

Answer the following questions.

a. Find the actual distance of the mall entrance, and determine whether the set panels will fit.

$$4\tfrac{1}{2} \times 3$$

$$\frac{9}{2} \times \frac{3}{1} \quad \frac{27}{2} = 13.5$$

Yes,

b. What is the scale factor? What does it tell us?

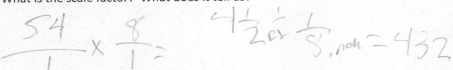

$$\frac{54}{1} \times \frac{8}{1} = \qquad 4\tfrac{1}{2} \text{ or } \tfrac{1}{8}, \text{noh} = 432$$

EUREKA
MATH™

Problem Set

1. A toy company is redesigning its packaging for model cars. The graphic design team needs to take the old image shown below and resize it so that $\frac{1}{2}$ inch on the old packaging represents $\frac{1}{3}$ inch on the new package. Find the length of the image on the new package.

   Car image length on old packaging measures 2 inches.

   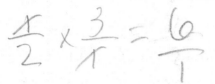

2. The city of St. Louis is creating a welcome sign on a billboard for visitors to see as they enter the city. The following picture needs to be enlarged so that $\frac{1}{2}$ inch represents 7 feet on the actual billboard. Will it fit on a billboard that measures 14 feet in height?

   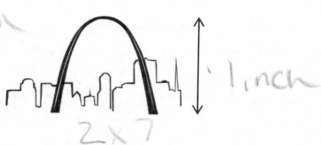

3. Your mom is repainting your younger brother's room. She is going to project the image shown below onto his wall so that she can paint an enlarged version as a mural. Use a ruler to determine the length of the image of the train. Then determine how long the mural will be if the projector uses a scale where 1 inch of the image represents $2\frac{1}{2}$ feet on the wall.

   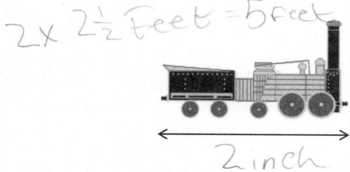

4. A model of a skyscraper is made so that 1 inch represents 75 feet. What is the height of the actual building if the height of the model is $18\frac{3}{5}$ inches?

5. The portrait company that takes little league baseball team photos is offering an option where a portrait of your baseball pose can be enlarged to be used as a wall decal (sticker). Your height in the portrait measures $3\frac{1}{2}$ inches. If the company uses a scale where 1 inch on the portrait represents 20 inches on the wall decal, find the height on the wall decal. Your actual height is 55 inches. If you stand next to the wall decal, will it be larger or smaller than you?

30 x 12   rectangle   reduction

6. The sponsor of a 5K run/walk for charity wishes to create a stamp of its billboard to commemorate the event. If the sponsor uses a scale where 1 inch represents 4 feet, and the billboard is a rectangle with a width of 14 feet and a length of 48 feet, what will be the shape and size of the stamp?

NO

20.5 x 25   12.5 x 10.5

7. Danielle is creating a scale drawing of her room. The rectangular room measures $20\frac{1}{2}$ ft. by 25 ft. If her drawing uses the scale where 1 inch represents 2 feet of the actual room, will her drawing fit on an $8\frac{1}{2}$ in. by 11 in. piece of paper?

8. A model of an apartment is shown below where $\frac{1}{4}$ inch represents 4 feet in the actual apartment. Use a ruler to measure the drawing and find the actual length and width of the bedroom.

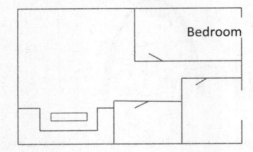

©2016 Great Minds. eureka-math.org
G7-M1M2-SE-B1-1.3.1-02.2016

EUREKA MATH

Lesson 19: Computing Actual Areas from a Scale Drawing

Classwork

Use the diagrams below to find the scale factor and then find the area of each figure.

Example 1

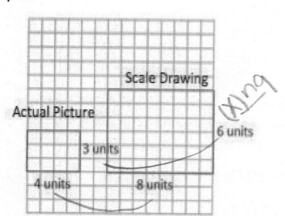

Scale factor: ___2___

Actual Area = ___12 units²___

Scale Drawing Area = ___48 units²___

Value of the Ratio of the Scale Drawing Area to the Actual Area: ___4___

Example 2

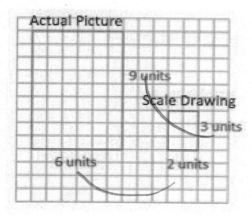

Scale factor: ___$\frac{1}{3}$___

Actual Area = ___54 units²___

Scale Drawing Area = ___6 units²___

Value of the Ratio of the Scale Drawing Area to the Actual Area: ___$\frac{6}{54} = \frac{1}{9}$___

Example 3

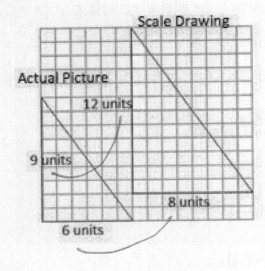

Scale factor: $\dfrac{8}{6} = \dfrac{4}{3}$

Actual Area = 27

Scale Drawing Area = 48

Value of the Ratio of the Scale Drawing Area to the

Actual Area: _____

$$\dfrac{48}{27} = \dfrac{16}{9}$$

Results: What do you notice about the ratio of the areas in Examples 1–3? Complete the statements below.

When the scale factor of the sides was 2, then the value of the ratio of the areas was _____. $4 \quad 2^2$

When the scale factor of the sides was $\dfrac{1}{3}$, then the value of the ratio of the areas was _____. $\dfrac{1}{9} \quad \left(\dfrac{1}{3}\right)$

When the scale factor of the sides was $\dfrac{4}{3}$, then the value of the ratio of the areas was _____. $\dfrac{16}{9} \quad \left(\dfrac{4}{3}\right)^2$

Based on these observations, what conclusion can you draw about scale factor and area?

If the scale factor of the sides is r, then the ratio of the areas is _____ R^2.

3, 9,

$$\dfrac{1}{4} \times \dfrac{1}{4} = \dfrac{1}{16}$$

EUREKA MATH

©2016 Great Minds. eureka-math.org
G7-M1M2-SE-B1-1.3.1-02.2016

Example 4: They Said Yes!

The Student Government liked your half-court basketball plan. They have asked you to calculate the actual area of the court so that they can estimate the cost of the project.

Based on your drawing below, what will the area of the planned half-court be?

Scale Drawing: 1 inch on the drawing corresponds to 15 feet of actual length

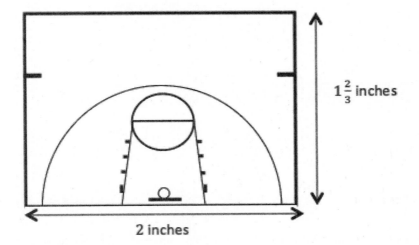

$1\frac{2}{3}$ inches

2 inches

A STORY OF RATIOS   Lesson 19 | 7•1

Does the actual area you found reflect the results we found from Examples 1–3? Explain how you know.

Exercises

1. The triangle depicted by the drawing has an actual area of 36 square units. What is the scale of the drawing?
    (Note: Each square on the grid has a length of 1 unit.)

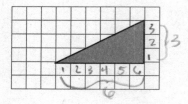

Scale Drawing Area: $\frac{1}{2}$ 6·3 = 9; 9 Sqaure unit

Ratio of Scale Drawing Area to Actal Area $\frac{9}{36}$ = r

therefore, R (Scale factor) = $\frac{3}{6}$ Since $\frac{3}{6} \cdot \frac{3}{6} = \frac{9}{36}$ the

Scale factor is $\frac{1}{2}$ the scale is unit of drawing

length.

©2016 Great Minds. eureka-math.org
G7-M1M2-SE-B1-1.3.1-02.2016

EUREKA
MATH

2. Use the scale drawings of two different apartments to answer the questions. Use a ruler to measure.

Suburban Apartment

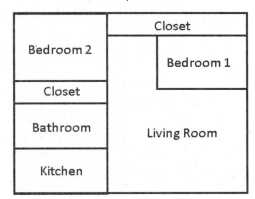

City Apartment

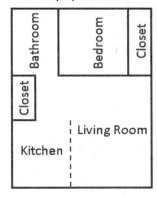

Scale: 1 inch on a scale drawing
corresponds to 12 feet in the
actual apartment.

Scale: 1 inch on a scale drawing
corresponds to 16 feet in the
actual apartment.

a. Find the scale drawing area for both apartments, and then use it to find the actual area of both apartments.

Scale Drawing (Square Inches)	$2\frac{1}{2}(2) = 5$	$(2)\,1\frac{1}{2} = 3$
Actual Area (Square feet)	$5(12) = 5(144)$ 720	$3(16^3) = 3 \cdot 256 =$ 768

b. Which apartment has closets with more square footage? Justify your thinking.

Scale Drawing Area Square inches	$(1\frac{1}{4}) + (1\frac{1}{4}\cdot\frac{1}{4})$ $= \frac{1}{4} + \frac{5}{8} + \frac{5}{8})$	$(\frac{1}{4}\,\frac{3}{4})(\frac{1}{2}\,\frac{1}{4})$ $= \frac{3}{6} + \frac{1}{8} + \frac{5}{16}$
Square feet	$(\frac{5}{8})\,144 = 90$	$(\frac{5}{16})(256) = 60$

c.   Which apartment has the largest bathroom? Justify your thinking.

d.   A one-year lease for the suburban apartment costs $750 per month. A one-year lease for the city apartment costs $925. Which apartment offers the greater value in terms of the cost per square foot?

Lesson 19:   Computing Actual Areas from a Scale Drawing

©2016 Great Minds. eureka-math.org
G7-M1M2-SE-B1-1.3.1-02.2016

EUREKA
MATH

Lesson Summary

Given the scale factor, r, representing the relationship between scale drawing length and actual length, the square of this scale factor, r^2, represents the relationship between the scale drawing area and the actual area.

For example, if 1 inch on the scale drawing represents 4 inches of actual length, then the scale factor, r, is $\frac{1}{4}$. On this same drawing, 1 square inch of scale drawing area would represent 16 square inches of actual area since r^2 is $\frac{1}{16}$.

Problem Set

1. The shaded rectangle shown below is a scale drawing of a rectangle whose area is 288 square feet. What is the scale factor of the drawing? (Note: Each square on the grid has a length of 1 unit.)

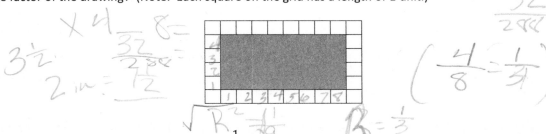

2. A floor plan for a home is shown below where $\frac{1}{2}$ inch corresponds to 6 feet of the actual home. Bedroom 2 belongs to 13-year-old Kassie, and Bedroom 3 belongs to 9-year-old Alexis. Kassie claims that her younger sister, Alexis, got the bigger bedroom. Is she right? Explain.

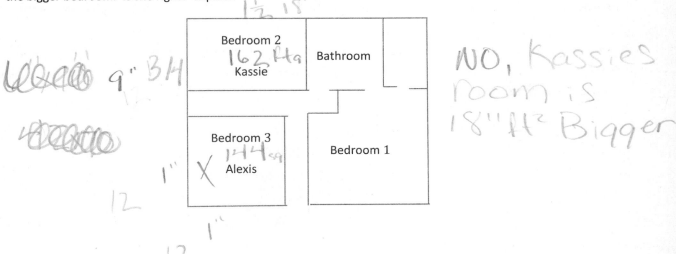

3. On the mall floor plan, $\frac{1}{4}$ inch represents 3 feet in the actual store.

    a. Find the actual area of Store 1 and Store 2.

    b. In the center of the atrium, there is a large circular water feature that has an area of $\left(\frac{9}{64}\right)\pi$ square inches on
        the drawing. Find the actual area in square feet.

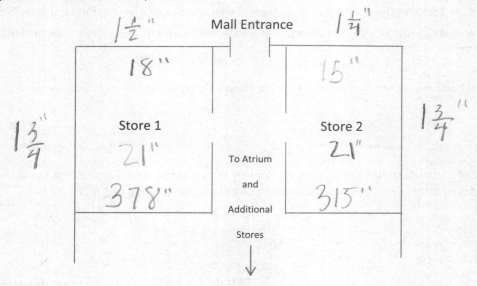

4. The greenhouse club is purchasing seed for the lawn in the school courtyard. The club needs to determine how
    much to buy. Unfortunately, the club meets after school, and students are unable to find a custodian to unlock the
    door. Anthony suggests they just use his school map to calculate the area that will need to be covered in seed. He
    measures the rectangular area on the map and finds the length to be 10 inches and the width to be 6 inches. The
    map notes the scale of 1 inch representing 7 feet in the actual courtyard. What is the actual area in square feet?

    6 × 10   42 × 70   42 × 70 = 2940 sq. ft

5. The company installing the new in-ground pool in your backyard has provided you with the scale drawing shown
    below. If the drawing uses a scale of 1 inch to $1\frac{3}{4}$ feet, calculate the total amount of two-dimensional space needed
    for the pool and its surrounding patio.

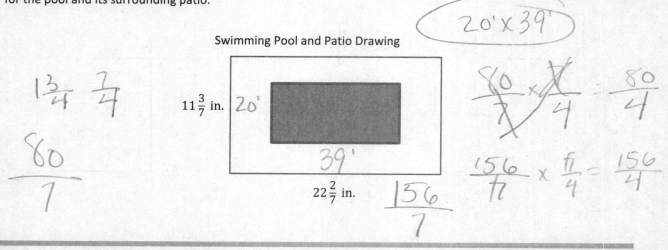

Lesson 20: An Exercise in Creating a Scale Drawing

Classwork

Today you will be applying your knowledge from working with scale drawings to create a floor plan for your idea of the dream classroom.

Exploratory Challenge: Your Dream Classroom

Guidelines

Take measurements: All students will work with the perimeter of the classroom as well as the doors and windows. Give students the dimensions of the room. Have students use the table provided to record the measurements.

Create your dream classroom, and use the furniture catalog to pick out your furniture: Students will discuss what their ideal classroom will look like with their partners and pick out furniture from the catalog. Students should record the actual measurements on the given table.

Determine the scale and calculate scale drawing lengths and widths: Each pair of students will determine its own scale. The calculation of the scale drawing lengths, widths, and areas is to be included.

Scale Drawing: Using a ruler and referring back to the calculated scale length, students will draw the scale drawing including the doors, windows, and furniture.

Measurements

	Classroom Perimeter	Windows	Door	Additional Furniture	CC	Table	Desk	SC	
Actual Length:	30'		82''	4 bia	3'	3'	3'	2'	
Width:	25'		46''	Table	2'	2'	5	2'	
Scale Drawing Length:									
Width:									

Scale: _____

Initial Sketch: Use this space to sketch the classroom perimeter, draw out your ideas, and play with the placement of the furniture.

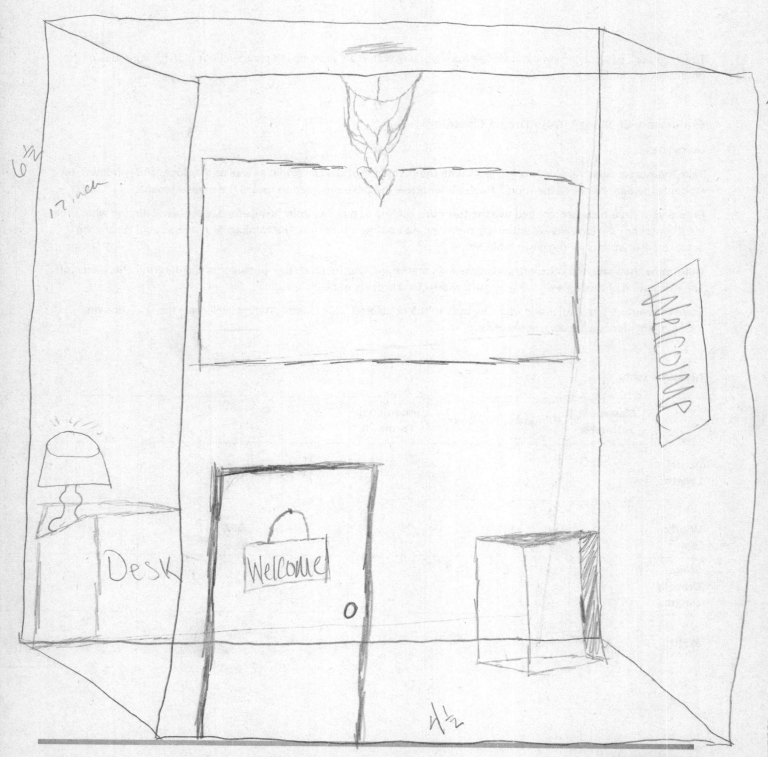

Lesson 20:   An Exercise in Creating a Scale Drawing

EUREKA
MATH™

Scale Drawing: Use a ruler and refer back to the calculated scale length, draw the scale drawing including the doors, windows, and furniture.

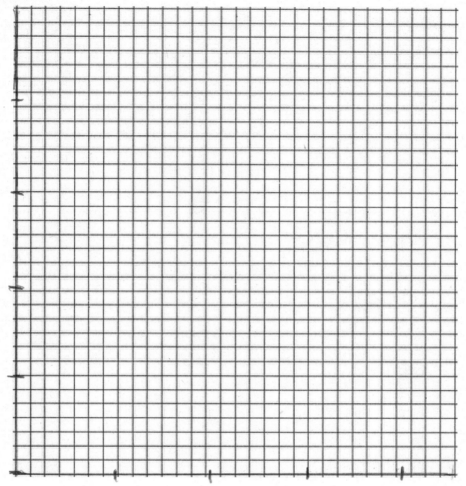

$1'' = 5''$

$2 =$

Area

	Classroom					
Actual Area:						
Scale Drawing Area:						

EUREKA MATH™

Lesson Summary

Scale Drawing Process:

1. Measure lengths and widths carefully with a ruler or tape measure. Record the measurements in an organized table.

2. Calculate the scale drawing lengths, widths, and areas using what was learned in previous lessons.

3. Calculate the actual areas.

4. Begin by drawing the perimeter, windows, and doorways.

5. Continue to draw the pieces of furniture making note of placement of objects (distance from nearest wall).

6. Check for reasonableness of measurements and calculations.

Problem Set

Interior Designer

You won a spot on a famous interior designing TV show! The designers will work with you and your existing furniture to redesign a room of your choice. Your job is to create a top-view scale drawing of your room and the furniture within it.

- With the scale factor being $\frac{1}{24}$, create a scale drawing of your room or other favorite room in your home on a sheet of 8.5×11-inch graph paper.

- Include the perimeter of the room, windows, doorways, and three or more furniture pieces (such as tables, desks, dressers, chairs, bed, sofa, ottoman, etc.).

- Use the table to record lengths and include calculations of areas.

- Make your furniture "moveable" by duplicating your scale drawing and cutting out the furniture.

- Create a "before" and "after" to help you decide how to rearrange your furniture. Take a photo of your "before."

- What changed in your furniture plans?

- Why do you like the "after" better than the "before"?

©2016 Great Minds. eureka-math.org
G7-M1M2-SE-B1-1.3.1-02.2016

	Entire Room	Windows	Doors	Desk/Tables	Seating	Storage	Bed		
Actual Length:									
Actual Width:									
Scale Drawing Length:									
Scale Drawing Width:									

	Entire Room Length	Desk/Tables	Seating	Storage	Bed		
Actual Area:							
Scale Drawing Area:							

EUREKA MATH

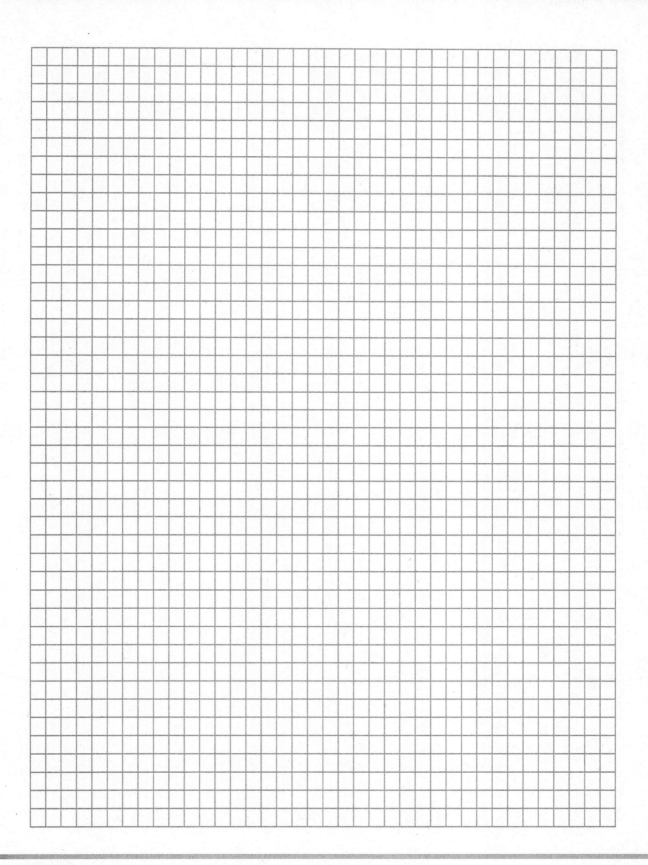

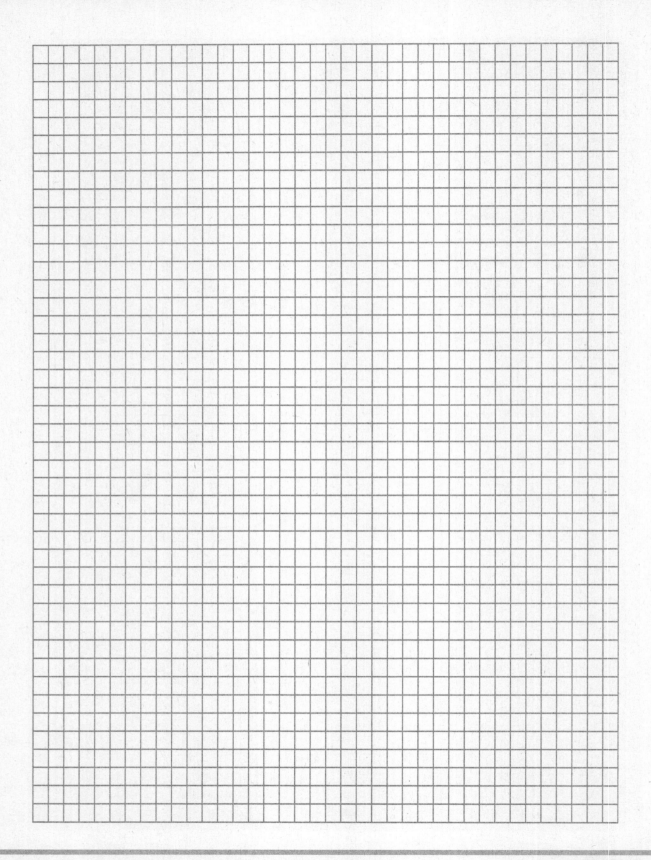

Lesson 20:   An Exercise in Creating a Scale Drawing

EUREKA MATH

©2016 Great Minds. eureka-math.org
G7-M1M2-SE-B1-1.3.1-02.2016

Lesson 21: An Exercise in Changing Scales

Classwork

How does your scale drawing change when a new scale factor is presented?

Exploratory Challenge: A New Scale Factor

The school plans to publish your work on the dream classroom in the next newsletter. Unfortunately, in order to fit the drawing on the page in the magazine, it must be $\frac{1}{4}$ its current length. Create a new drawing ($SD2$) in which all of the lengths are $\frac{1}{4}$ those in the original scale drawing ($SD1$) from Lesson 20.

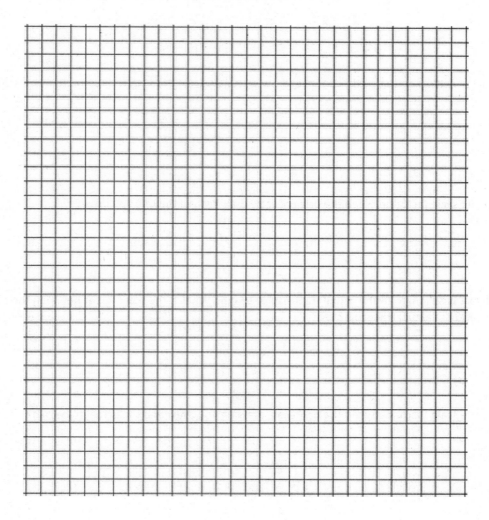

Exercise

The picture shows an enlargement or reduction of a scale drawing of a trapezoid.

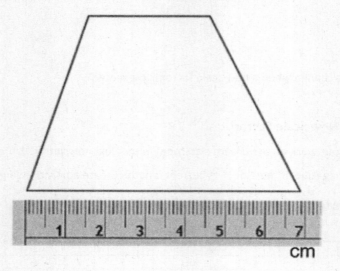

Using the scale factor written on the card you chose, draw your new scale drawing with correctly calculated measurements.

a. What is the scale factor between the original scale drawing and the one you drew?

b. The longest base length of the actual trapezoid is 10 cm. What is the scale factor between the original scale drawing and the actual trapezoid?

c. What is the scale factor between the new scale drawing you drew and the actual trapezoid?

EUREKA
MATH™

©2016 Great Minds. eureka-math.org
G7-M1M2-SE-B1-1.3.1-02.2016

Changing Scale Factors:

- To produce a scale drawing at a different scale, you must determine the new scale factor. The new scale factor is found by dividing the different (new drawing) scale factor by the original scale factor.

- To find each new length, you can multiply each length in the original scale drawing by this new scale factor.

Steps:

- Find each scale factor.

- Divide the new scale factor by the original scale factor.

- Divide the given length by the new scale factor (the quotient from the prior step).

©2016 Great Minds. eureka-math.org
G7-M1M2-SE-B1-1.3.1-02.2016

Lesson Summary

Variations of Scale Drawings with different scale factors are scale drawings of an original scale drawing.

From a scale drawing at a different scale, the scale factor for the original scale drawing can be computed without information of the actual object, figure, or picture.

- For example, if *scale drawing one* has a scale factor of $\frac{1}{24}$ and *scale drawing two* has a scale factor of $\frac{1}{72}$, then the scale factor relating *scale drawing two* to *scale drawing one* is

$$\frac{1}{72} \text{ to } \frac{1}{24} = \frac{\frac{1}{72}}{\frac{1}{24}} = \frac{1}{72} \cdot \frac{24}{1} = \frac{1}{3}.$$

- *Scale drawing two* has lengths that are $\frac{1}{3}$ the size of the lengths of *scale drawing one*.

Problem Set

1. Jake reads the following problem: If the original scale factor for a scale drawing of a square swimming pool is $\frac{1}{90}$, and the length of the original drawing measured to be 8 inches, what is the length on the new scale drawing if the scale factor of the new scale drawing length to actual length is $\frac{1}{144}$?

   He works out the problem:

   8 inches $\div \frac{1}{90} = 720$ inches

   720 inches $\times \frac{1}{144} = 5$ inches

   Is he correct? Explain why or why not.

2. What is the scale factor of the new scale drawing to the original scale drawing ($SD2$ to $SD1$)?

3. Using the scale, if the length of the pool measures 10 cm on the new scale drawing:

   a. Using the scale factor from Problem 1, $\frac{1}{144}$, find the actual length of the pool in meters.

   b. What is the surface area of the floor of the actual pool? Rounded to the nearest tenth.

   c. If the pool has a constant depth of 1.5 meters, what is the volume of the pool? Rounded to the nearest tenth.

   d. If 1 cubic meter of water is equal to 264.2 gallons, how much water will the pool contain when completely filled? Rounded to the nearest unit.

4. Complete a new scale drawing of your dream room from the Problem Set in Lesson 20 by either reducing by $\frac{1}{4}$ or enlarging it by 4.

©2016 Great Minds. eureka-math.org
G7-M1M2-SE-B1-1.3.1-02.2016

Lesson 22: An Exercise in Changing Scales

Classwork

Exploratory Challenge: Reflection on Scale Drawings

Using the new scale drawing of your dream room, list the similarities and differences between this drawing and the original drawing completed for Lesson 20.

<u>Similarities</u>   <u>Differences</u>

Original Scale Factor: _____   New Scale Factor: _____

What is the relationship between these scale factors?

Key Idea:

Two different scale drawings of the same top-view of a room are also scale drawings of each other. In other words, a scale drawing of a different scale can also be considered a scale drawing of the original scale drawing.

©2016 Great Minds. eureka-math.org
G7-M1M2-SE-B1-1.3.1-02.2016

Example 1: Building a Bench

To surprise her mother, Taylor helped her father build a bench for the front porch. Taylor's father had the instructions with drawings, but Taylor wanted to have her own copy. She enlarged her copy to make it easier to read. Using the following diagram, fill in the missing information. To complete the first row of the table, write the scale factor of the bench to the bench, the bench to the original diagram, and the bench to Taylor's diagram. Complete the remaining rows similarly.

The pictures below show the diagram of the bench shown on the original instructions and the diagram of the bench shown on Taylor's enlarged copy of the instruction.

Original Drawing of Bench (top view)   Taylor's Drawing (top view)

                                                                    Scale factor to the bench: 12

        2 inches   6 inches

Scale Factors

	Bench	Original Diagram	Taylor's Diagram
Bench	1		
Original Diagram		1	
Taylor's Diagram			1

Exercise 1

Carmen and Jackie were driving separately to a concert. Jackie printed a map of the directions on a piece of paper before the drive, and Carmen took a picture of Jackie's map on her phone. Carmen's map had a scale factor to the actual distance of $\dfrac{1}{563,270}$. Using the pictures, what is the scale of Carmen's map to Jackie's map? What was the scale factor of Jackie's printed map to the actual distance?

Jackie's Map   Carmen's Map

26 cm

                                                                    4 cm

EUREKA
MATH

©2016 Great Minds. eureka-math.org
G7-M1M2-SE-B1-1.3.1-02.2016

Exercise 2

Ronald received a special toy train set for his birthday. In the picture of the train on the package, the boxcar has the following dimensions: length is $4\frac{5}{16}$ inches; width is $1\frac{1}{8}$ inches; and height is $1\frac{5}{8}$ inches. The toy boxcar that Ronald received has dimensions l is 17.25 inches; w is 4.5 inches; and h is 6.5 inches. If the actual boxcar is 50 feet long:

a. Find the scale factor of the picture on the package to the toy set.

b. Find the scale factor of the picture on the package to the actual boxcar.

c. Use these two scale factors to find the scale factor between the toy set and the actual boxcar.

d. What are the width and height of the actual boxcar?

Lesson Summary

The scale drawing of a different scale is a scale drawing of the original scale drawing.

To find the scale factor for the original drawing, write a ratio to compare the drawing length from the original drawing to its corresponding actual length from the second scale drawing.

Refer to the example below where we compare the drawing length from the Original Scale drawing to its corresponding actual length from the New Scale drawing:

6 inches represents 12 feet or 0.5 feet represent 12 feet

This gives an equivalent ratio of $\frac{1}{24}$ for the scale factor of the original drawing.

Original Scale Drawing:

(unknown SF)

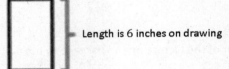

Length is 6 inches on drawing

New Scale Drawing (different scale):

1 inch represents 6 feet

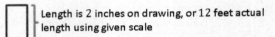

Length is 2 inches on drawing, or 12 feet actual length using given scale

Problem Set

1. For the scale drawing, the actual lengths are labeled onto the scale drawing. Measure the lengths, in centimeters, of the scale drawing with a ruler, and draw a new scale drawing with a scale factor (SD2 to SD1) of $\frac{1}{2}$.

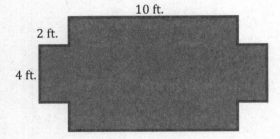

10 ft.

2 ft.

4 ft.

EUREKA
MATH™

2. Compute the scale factor of the new scale drawing (SD2) to the first scale drawing (SD1) using the information from the given scale drawings.

a.   Original Scale Factor: $\dfrac{6}{35}$ New Scale Factor: $\dfrac{1}{280}$

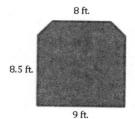

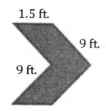

Scale Factor: _____

b.   Original Scale Factor: $\dfrac{1}{12}$ New Scale Factor: 3

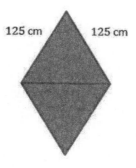

Scale Factor: _____

c.   Original Scale Factor: 20   New Scale Factor: 25

Scale Factor: _____

This page intentionally left blank

Eureka Math
Grade 7
Module 2

Special thanks go to the Gordon A. Cain Center and to the Department of Mathematics at Louisiana State University for their support in the development of *Eureka Math*.

Lesson 1: Opposite Quantities Combine to Make Zero

Classwork

Exercise 1: Positive and Negative Numbers Review

With your partner, use the graphic organizer below to record what you know about positive and negative numbers. Add or remove statements during the whole-class discussion.

Negative Numbers   **Positive Numbers**

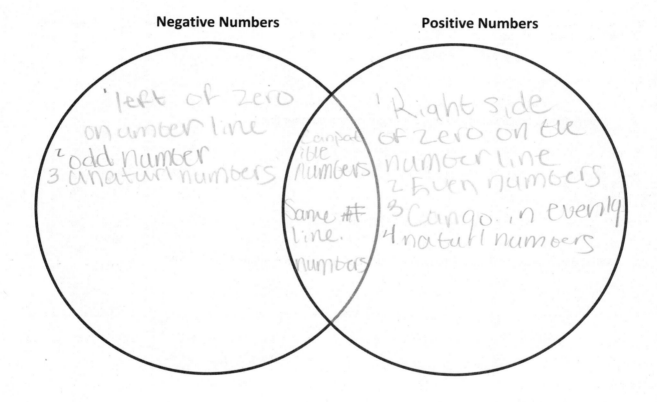

1 left of zero on number line
2 odd number
3 unnatural numbers

Compatible Numbers

Same # line. numbers

1 Right side of zero on the number line
2 Even numbers
3 Can go in evenly
4 natural numbers

Example 2: Counting Up and Counting Down on the Number Line

Use the number line below to practice counting up and counting down.

- *Counting up* starting at 0 corresponds to _____*Positive*_____ numbers.

- *Counting down* starting at 0 corresponds to _____*Negative*_____ numbers.

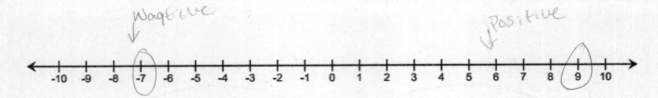

a.   Where do you begin when locating a number on the number line?

   Zero

b.   What do you call the distance between a number and 0 on a number line?

   Absolute Value

c.   What is the relationship between 7 and −7?

   Opposites

Example 3: Using the Integer Game and the Number Line

What is the sum of the card values shown? Use the counting on method on the provided number line to justify your answer.

| 5 | −5 | −4 | 8 |

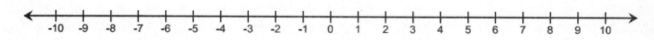

a.   What is the final position on the number line? _____ 4

b.   What card or combination of cards would you need to get back to 0? _____ −4

Exercise 2: The ⟮Additive Inverse⟯

Use the number line to answer each of the following questions.

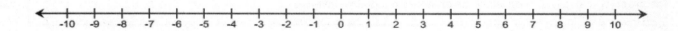

a.   How far is 7 from 0 and in which direction? _____ 7 to the right

b.   What is the opposite of 7? _____ −7

c.   How far is −7 from 0 and in which direction? _____ 7 to the left

d. Thinking back to our previous work, explain how you would use the counting on method to represent the following: While playing the Integer Game, the first card selected is 7, and the second card selected is −7.

e. What does this tell us about the sum of 7 and its opposite, −7?

f. Look at the curved arrows you drew for 7 and −7. What relationship exists between these two arrows that would support your claim about the sum of 7 and −7?

g. Do you think this will hold true for the sum of any number and its opposite? Why?

Property: For every number a, there is a number $-a$ so that $a + (-a) = 0$ and $(-a) + a = 0$.

The *additive inverse of a number* is a number such that the sum of the two numbers is 0. The opposite of a number satisfies this definition: For example, the opposite of 3 is −3, and $3 + (-3) = 0$. Hence −3 is the additive inverse of 3.

The property above is usually called the existence of additive inverses.

Exercise 3: Playing the Integer Game

Play the Integer Game with your group. Use a number line to practice counting on.

EUREKA
MATH™

Lesson Summary

- Add a positive number to a number by counting up from that number, and add a negative number to a number by counting down from that number.
- An integer plus its opposite sum to zero.
- The opposite of a number is called the additive inverse because the two numbers' sum is zero.

Problem Set

For Problems 1 and 2, refer to the Integer Game.

1. You have two cards with a sum of (-12) in your hand.
   a. What two cards could you have?
   b. You add two more cards to your hand, but the total sum of the cards remains the same, (-12). Give some different examples of two cards you could choose.

2. Choose one card value and its additive inverse. Choose from the list below to write a real-world story problem that would model their sum.
   a. Elevation: above and below sea level
   b. Money: credits and debits, deposits and withdrawals
   c. Temperature: above and below 0 degrees
   d. Football: loss and gain of yards

3. On the number line below, the numbers h and k are the same distance from 0. Write an equation to express the value of $h + k$. Explain.

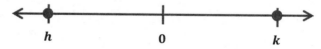

4. During a football game, Kevin gained five yards on the first play. Then he lost seven yards on the second play. How many yards does Kevin need on the next play to get the team back to where they were when they started? Show your work.

5. Write an addition number sentence that corresponds to the arrows below.

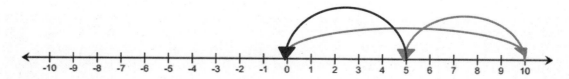

This page intentionally left blank

Lesson 2: Using the Number Line to Model the Addition of Integers

Classwork

Exercise 1: Real-World Introduction to Integer Addition

Answer the questions below.

a. Suppose you received $10 from your grandmother for your birthday. You spent $4 on snacks. Using addition, how would you write an equation to represent this situation?

$$(+10) + (-4) = (+6)$$

b. How would you model your equation on a number line to show your answer?

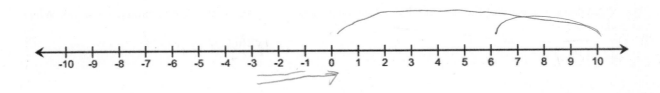

Example 1: Modeling Addition on the Number Line

Complete the steps to find the sum of $-2 + 3$ by filling in the blanks. Model the equation using straight arrows called *vectors* on the number line below.

a. Place the tail of the arrow on ___0___.

b. Draw the arrow 2 units to the left of 0, and stop at ___−2___. The direction of the arrow is to the ___left___ since you are counting down from 0.

c. Start the next arrow at the end of the first arrow, or at ___−2___.

d. Draw the second arrow ___3___ units to the right since you are counting up from -2.

e. Stop at ___+1___.

f.   Circle the number at which the second arrow ends to indicate the ending value.

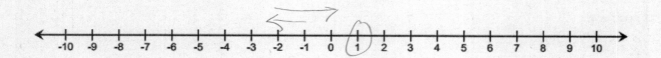

g.   Repeat the process from parts (a)–(f) for the expression $3 + (-2)$.

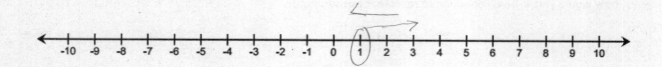

h.   What can you say about the sum of $-2 + 3$ and $3 + (-2)$? Does order matter when adding numbers? Why or why not?

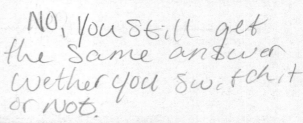

NO, you still get the same answer wether you switch it or not.

Example 2: Expressing Absolute Value as the Length of an Arrow on the Real Number Line

a.   How does absolute value determine the arrow length for -2? Use the number line provided to support your answer.

NO, because you have to maser

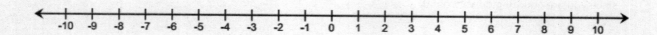

©2016 Great Minds. eureka-math.org
G7-M1M2-SE-B1-1.3.1-02.2016

EUREKA
MATH

b. How does the absolute value determine the arrow length for 3? Use the number line provided to support your answer.

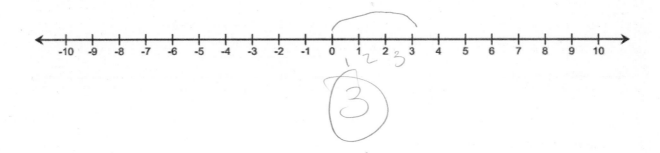

c. Describe how the absolute value helps you represent −10 on a number line.

Exercise 2

Create a number line model to represent each of the expressions below.

a. −6 + 4

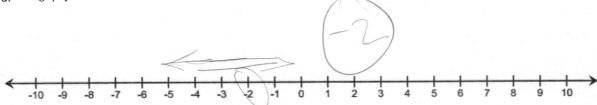

b. 3 + (−8)

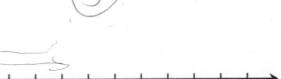

Example 3: Finding Sums on a Real Number Line Model

Find the sum of the integers represented in the diagram below.

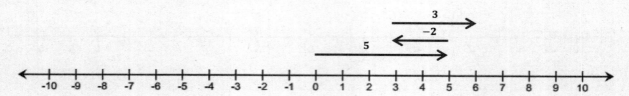

a. Write an equation to express the sum.

$$5 + -2 + 3 = 6$$

b. What three cards are represented in this model? How did you know?

5 -2 3 6

c. In what ways does this model differ from the ones we used in Lesson 1?

d. Can you make a connection between the sum of 6 and where the third arrow ends on the number line?

Yeah there the same but one is oppiste.

e. Would the sum change if we changed the order in which we add the numbers, for example, $(-2) + 3 + 5$?

NO

order dose not matter it addtion

f. Would the diagram change? If so, how?

Yes because your ganna end up the same th

Exercise 3

Play the Integer Game with your group. Use a number line to practice counting on.

EUREKA MATH™

Lesson Summary

- On a number line, arrows are used to represent integers; they show length and direction.
- The length of an arrow on the number line is the absolute value of the integer.
- Adding several arrows is the same as combining integers in the Integer Game.
- The sum of several arrows is the final position of the last arrow.

Problem Set

Represent Problems 1–3 using both a number line diagram and an equation.

1. David and Victoria are playing the Integer Card Game. David drew three cards, −6, 12, and −4. What is the sum of the cards in his hand? Model your answer on the number line below.

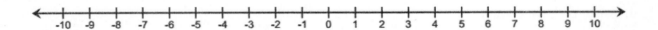

2. In the Integer Card Game, you drew the cards, 2, 8, and −11. Your partner gave you a 7 from his hand.
   a. What is your total? Model your answer on the number line below.

   b. What card(s) would you need to get your score back to zero? Explain. Use and explain the term *additive inverse* in your answer.

3. If a football player gains 40 yards on a play, but on the next play, he loses 10 yards, what would his total yards be for the game if he ran for another 60 yards? What did you count by to label the units on your number line?

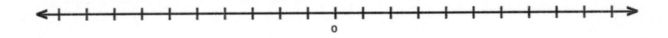

4. Find the sums.
    a. $-2 + 9$
    b. $-8 + -8$
    c. $-4 + (-6) + 10$
    d. $5 + 7 + (-11)$

5. Mark an integer between 1 and 5 on a number line, and label it point Z. Then, locate and label each of the following points by finding the sums.

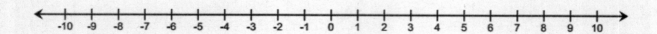

    a.   Point A: $Z + 5$
    b.   Point B: $Z + (-3)$
    c.   Point C: $(-4) + (-2) + Z$
    d.   Point D: $-3 + Z + 1$

6. Write a story problem that would model the sum of the arrows in the number diagram below.

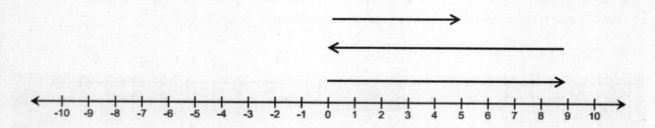

7. Do the arrows correctly represent the equation $4 + (-7) + 5 = 2$? If not, draw a correct model below.

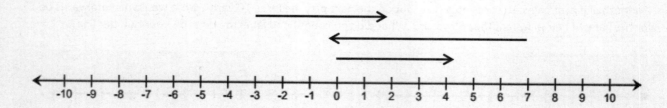

EUREKA
MATH™

©2016 Great Minds. eureka-math.org
G7-M1M2-SE-B1-1.3.1-02.2016

Lesson 3: Understanding Addition of Integers

Classwork

Exercise 1: Addition Using the Integer Game

Play the Integer Game with your group without using a number line.

Example 1: Counting On to Express the Sum as Absolute Value on a Number Line

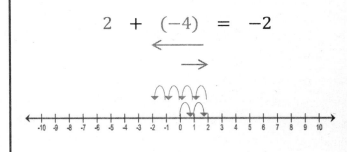

Counting up −4 is the same as *the opposite of counting up* 4 and also means counting down 4.

a. For each example above, what is the distance between 2 and the sum?

b. Does the sum lie to the right or left of 2 on a horizontal number line? Above or below on a vertical number line?

c. Given the expression $54 + 81$, determine, without finding the sum, the distance between 54 and the sum. Explain.

d. Is the sum to the right or left of 54 on the horizontal number line? Above or below on a vertical number line?

e. Given the expression $14 + (-3)$, determine, without finding the sum, the distance between 14 and the sum. Explain.

f. Is the sum to the right or left of 14 on the number line? Above or below on a vertical number line?

Exercise 2

Work with a partner to create a horizontal number line model to represent each of the following expressions. What is the sum?

a. $-5 + 3$

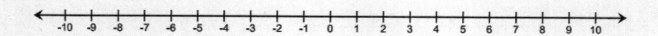

EUREKA
MATH™

©2016 Great Minds. eureka-math.org
G7-M1M2-SE-B1-1.3.1-02.2016

b. $-6 + (-2)$

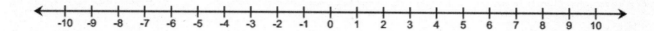

c. $7 + (-8)$

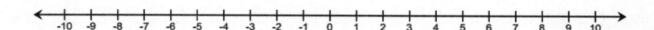

Exercise 3: Writing an Equation Using Verbal Descriptions

Write an equation, and using the number line, create an *arrow diagram* given the following information:

The sum of 6 and a number is 15 units to the left of 6 on the number line.

Equation:

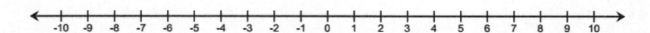

Lesson Summary

- Adding an integer to a number can be represented on a number line as counting up when the integer is positive (just like whole numbers) and counting down when the integer is negative.

- Arrows can be used to represent the sum of two integers on a number line.

Problem Set

1. Below is a table showing the change in temperature from morning to afternoon for one week.

   a. Use the vertical number line to help you complete the table. As an example, the first row is completed for you.

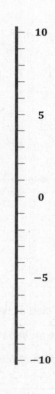

Change in Temperatures from Morning to Afternoon

Morning Temperature	Change	Afternoon Temperature	Equation
1°C	Rise of 3°C	4°C	$1 + 3 = 4$
2°C	Rise of 8°C		
−2°C	Fall of 6°C		
−4°C	Rise of 7°C		
6°C	Fall of 9°C		
−5°C	Fall of 5°C		
7°C	Fall of 7°C		

   b. Do you agree or disagree with the following statement: "A rise of −7°C" means "a fall of 7°C"? Explain. (Note: No one would ever say, "A rise of −7 degrees"; however, mathematically speaking, it is an equivalent phrase.)

For Problems 2–3, refer to the Integer Game.

2. Terry selected two cards. The sum of her cards is −10.

   a. Can both cards be positive? Explain why or why not.

   b. Can one of the cards be positive and the other be negative? Explain why or why not.

   c. Can both cards be negative? Explain why or why not.

©2016 Great Minds. eureka-math.org
G7-M1M2-SE-B1-1.3.1-02.2016

3. When playing the Integer Game, the first two cards you selected were −8 and −10.

    a. What is the value of your hand? Write an equation to justify your answer.

    b. For part (a), what is the distance of the sum from −8? Does the sum lie to the right or left of −8 on the number line?

    c. If you discarded the −10 and then selected a 10, what would be the value of your hand? Write an equation to justify your answer.

4. Given the expression 67 + (−35), can you determine, without finding the sum, the distance between 67 and the sum? Is the sum to the right or left of 67 on the number line?

5. Use the information given below to write an equation. Then create an *arrow diagram* of this equation on the number line provided below.

    The sum of −4 and a number is 12 units to the right of −4 on a number line.

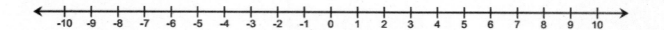

EUREKA
MATH™

Lesson 3:   Understanding Addition of Integers

S.17

©2016 Great Minds. eureka-math.org
G7-M1M2-SE-B1-1.3.1-02.2016

This page intentionally left blank

Lesson 4: Efficiently Adding Integers and Other Rational Numbers

Classwork

Example 1: Rule for Adding Integers with Same Signs

a.   Represent the sum of $3 + 5$ using arrows on the number line.

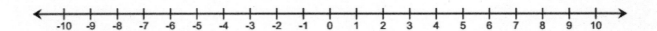

   i.   How long is the arrow that represents 3?

   ii.   What direction does it point?

   iii.   How long is the arrow that represents 5?

   iv.   What direction does it point?

   v.   What is the sum?

   vi.   If you were to represent the sum using an arrow, how long would the arrow be, and what direction would it point?

vii.   What is the relationship between the arrow representing the number on the number line and the absolute value of the number?

viii.   Do you think that adding two positive numbers will always give you a greater positive number? Why?

b.   Represent the sum of $-3 + (-5)$ using arrows that represent -3 and -5 on the number line.

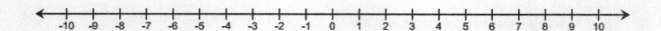

i.   How long is the arrow that represents -3?

ii.   What direction does it point?

iii.   How long is the arrow that represents -5?

iv.   What direction does it point?

v.   What is the sum?

EUREKA
MATH™

vi.   If you were to represent the sum using an arrow, how long would the arrow be, and what direction would it point?

vii. Do you think that adding two negative numbers will always give you a smaller negative number? Why?

c.   What do both examples have in common?

RULE: Add rational numbers with the same sign by adding the absolute values and using the common sign.

Exercise 2

a.   Decide whether the sum will be positive or negative without actually calculating the sum.

   i. $-4 + (-2)$ _____

   ii. $5 + 9$ _____

   iii. $-6 + (-3)$ _____

   iv. $-1 + (-11)$ _____

   v. $3 + 5 + 7$ _____

   vi. $-20 + (-15)$ _____

b. Find the sum.

   i. $15 + 7$

   ii. $-4 + (-16)$

   iii. $-18 + (-64)$

   iv. $-205 + (-123)$

Example 2: Rule for Adding Opposite Signs

a. Represent $5 + (-3)$ using arrows on the number line.

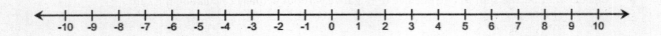

   i.   How long is the arrow that represents 5?

   ii. What direction does it point?

   iii. How long is the arrow that represents -3?

   iv. What direction does it point?

EUREKA
MATH™

©2016 Great Minds. eureka-math.org
G7-M1M2-SE-B1-1.3.1-02.2016

    v.   Which arrow is longer?

    vi.   What is the sum? If you were to represent the sum using an arrow, how long would the arrow be, and what direction would it point?

b.   Represent the $4 + (-7)$ using arrows on the number line.

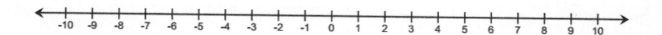

    i.   In the two examples above, what is the relationship between the length of the arrow representing the sum and the lengths of the arrows representing the two addends?

    ii.   What is the relationship between the direction of the arrow representing the sum and the direction of the arrows representing the two addends?

    iii.   Write a rule that will give the length and direction of the arrow representing the sum of two values that have opposite signs.

RULE: *Add rational numbers with opposite signs by subtracting the absolute values and using the sign of the integer with the greater absolute value.*

 Lesson 4:   Efficiently Adding Integers and Other Rational Numbers   **S.23**

©2016 Great Minds. eureka-math.org
G7-M1M2-SE-B1-1.3.1-02.2016

Exercise 3

a. Circle the integer with the greater absolute value. Decide whether the sum will be positive or negative without actually calculating the sum.

   i. $-1 + 2$ _____

   ii. $5 + (-9)$ _____

   iii. $-6 + 3$ _____

   iv. $-11 + 1$ _____

b. Find the sum.

   i. $-10 + 7$

   ii. $8 + (-16)$

   iii. $-12 + (65)$

   iv. $105 + (-126)$

Example 3: Applying Integer Addition Rules to Rational Numbers

Find the sum of $6 + \left(-2\frac{1}{4}\right)$. The addition of rational numbers follows the same rules of addition for integers.

a.   Find the absolute values of the numbers.

b.   Subtract the absolute values.

c.   The answer will take the sign of the number that has the greater absolute value.

Exercise 4

Solve the following problems. Show your work.

a.   Find the sum of $-18 + 7$.

b.   If the temperature outside was 73 degrees at 5:00 p.m., but it fell 19 degrees by 10:00 p.m., what is the temperature at 10:00 p.m.? Write an equation and solve.

c.   Write an addition sentence, and find the sum using the diagram below.

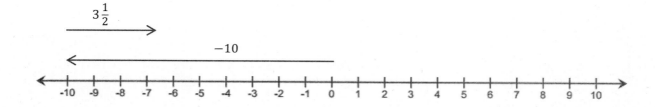

Lesson Summary

- Add integers with the same sign by adding the absolute values and using the common sign.
- Steps to adding integers with opposite signs:
    1. Find the absolute values of the integers.
    2. Subtract the absolute values.
    3. The answer will take the sign of the integer that has the greater absolute value.
- To add rational numbers, follow the same rules used to add integers.

Problem Set

1. Find the sum. Show your work to justify your answer.
    a. $4 + 17$
    b. $-6 + (-12)$
    c. $2.2 + (-3.7)$
    d. $-3 + (-5) + 8$
    e. $\frac{1}{3} + \left(-2\frac{1}{4}\right)$

2. Which of these story problems describes the sum $19 + (-12)$? Check all that apply. Show your work to justify your answer.

    _____ Jared's dad paid him \$19 for raking the leaves from the yard on Wednesday. Jared spent \$12 at the movie theater on Friday. How much money does Jared have left?

    _____ Jared owed his brother \$19 for raking the leaves while Jared was sick. Jared's dad gave him \$12 for doing his chores for the week. How much money does Jared have now?

    _____ Jared's grandmother gave him \$19 for his birthday. He bought \$8 worth of candy and spent another \$4 on a new comic book. How much money does Jared have left over?

3. Use the diagram below to complete each part.

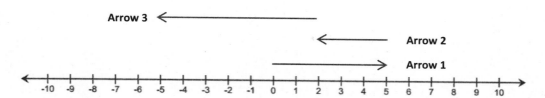

a. Label each arrow with the number the arrow represents.

b. How long is each arrow? What direction does each arrow point?

Arrow	Length	Direction
1		
2		
3		

c. Write an equation that represents the sum of the numbers. Find the sum.

4. Jennifer and Katie were playing the Integer Game in class. Their hands are represented below.

Jennifer's Hand   Katie's Hand

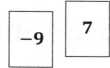

a. What is the value of each of their hands? Show your work to support your answer.

b. If Jennifer drew two more cards, is it possible for the value of her hand not to change? Explain why or why not.

c. If Katie wanted to win the game by getting a score of 0, what card would she need? Explain.

d. If Jennifer drew −1 and −2, what would be her new score? Show your work to support your answer.

This page intentionally left blank

Lesson 5: Understanding Subtraction of Integers and Other Rational Numbers

Classwork

Example 1: Exploring Subtraction with the Integer Game

Play the Integer Game in your group. Start Round 1 by selecting four cards. Follow the steps for each round of play.

1. Write the value of your hand in the Total column.
2. Then, record what card values you select in the Action 1 column and discard from your hand in the Action 2 column.
3. After each action, calculate your new total, and record it under the appropriate Results column.
4. Based on the results, describe what happens to the value of your hand under the appropriate Descriptions column. For example, "Score increased by 3."

Round	Total	Action 1	Result 1	Description	Action 2	Result 2	Description
1							
2							
3							
4							
5							

Discussion: Making Connections to Integer Subtraction

1. How did selecting positive value cards change the value of your hand?

2. How did selecting negative value cards change the value of your hand?

3. How did discarding positive value cards change the value of your hand?

4. How did discarding negative value cards change the value of your hand?

5. What operation reflects selecting a card?

6. What operation reflects discarding or removing a card?

7. Based on the game, can you make a prediction about what happens to the result when
   a. Subtracting a positive integer?

   b. Subtracting a negative integer?

At the end of the lesson, the class reviews its predictions.

EUREKA
MATH™

©2016 Great Minds. eureka-math.org
G7-M1M2-SE-B1-1.3.1-02.2016

Example 2: Subtracting a Positive Number

Follow along with your teacher to complete the diagrams below.

$$4 + 2 = \boxed{}$$

Show that discarding (subtracting) a positive card, which is the same as subtracting a positive number, decreases the value of the hand.

$$4 + 2 - 2 = \boxed{}$$

OR

$$4 + 2 + (-2) = \boxed{}$$

Removing (_____) a positive card changes the score in the same way as _____ a card whose value is the _____ _____ (or opposite). In this case, adding the corresponding

_____.

Example 3: Subtracting a Negative Number

Follow along with your teacher to complete the diagrams below.

4 -2

$4 + (-2) = \boxed{}$

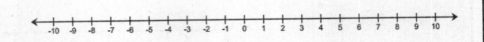

How does removing a negative card change the score, or value, of the hand?

4 $\cancel{-2}$

$4 + (-2) - (-2) = \boxed{}$

OR

4 -2 2

$4 + (-2) + 2 = \boxed{}$

Removing (_____) a negative card changes the score in the same way as _____ a card whose value is the _____   _____ (or opposite). In this case, adding the corresponding _____.

> **THE RULE OF SUBTRACTION:** *Subtracting a number is the same as adding its additive inverse (or opposite).*

Exercises 1–3: Subtracting Positive and Negative Integers

1. Using the rule of subtraction, rewrite the following subtraction sentences as addition sentences and solve. Use the number line below if needed.

   a. $8 - 2$

   b. $4 - 9$

   c. $-3 - 7$

   d. $-9 - (-2)$

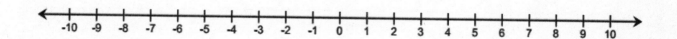

2. Find the differences.

   a. $-2 - (-5)$

   b. $11 - (-8)$

   c. $-10 - (-4)$

3. Write two equivalent expressions that represent the situation. What is the difference in their elevations?
   An airplane flies at an altitude of 25,000 feet. A submarine dives to a depth of 600 feet below sea level.

Lesson Summary

- **THE RULE OF SUBTRACTION:** Subtracting a number is the same as adding its opposite.
- Removing (subtracting) a positive card changes the score in the same way as adding a corresponding negative card.
- Removing (subtracting) a negative card makes the same change as adding the corresponding positive card.
- For all rational numbers, subtracting a number and adding it back gets you back to where you started: $(m - n) + n = m$.

Problem Set

1. On a number line, find the difference of each number and 4. Complete the table to support your answers. The first example is provided.

Number	Subtraction Expression	Addition Expression	Answer
10	$10 - 4$	$10 + (-4)$	6
2			
-4			
-6			
1			

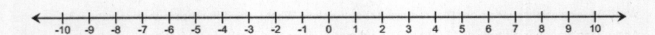

EUREKA MATH™

2. You and your partner were playing the Integer Game in class. Here are the cards in both hands.

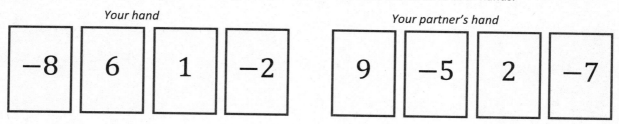

Your hand   *Your partner's hand*

-8 6   1 -2 9 -5 2 -7

    a.   Find the value of each hand. Who would win based on the current scores? (The score closest to 0 wins.)
    b.   Find the value of each hand if you discarded the -2 and selected a 5, and your partner discarded the -5 and selected a 5. Show your work to support your answer.
    c.   Use your score values from part (b) to determine who would win the game now.

3. Write the following expressions as a single integer.
    a. $-2 + 16$
    b. $-2 - (-16)$
    c. $18 - 26$
    d. $-14 - 23$
    e. $30 - (-45)$

4. Explain what is meant by the following, and illustrate with an example:

    "For any real numbers, p and q, $p - q = p + (-q)$."

5. Choose an integer between -1 and -5 on the number line, and label it point P. Locate and label the following points on the number line. Show your work.

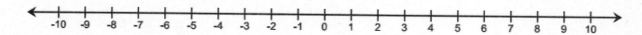

    a.   Point A: $P - 5$
    b.   Point B: $(P - 4) + 4$
    c.   Point C: $-P - (-7)$

Challenge Problem:

6. Write two equivalent expressions that represent the situation. What is the difference in their elevations?
    An airplane flies at an altitude of 26,000 feet. A submarine dives to a depth of 700 feet below sea level.

This page intentionally left blank

Lesson 6: The Distance Between Two Rational Numbers

Classwork

Exercise 1

Use the number line to answer each of the following.

Person A	Person B
What is the distance between −4 and 5?	What is the distance between 5 and −4?
What is the distance between −5 and −3?	What is the distance between −3 and −5?
What is the distance between 7 and −1?	What is the distance between −1 and 7?

EUREKA
MATH™

Exercise 2

Use the number line to answer each of the following questions.

    a.   What is the distance between 0 and −8?

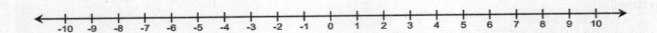

    b.   What is the distance between −2 and $-1\frac{1}{2}$?

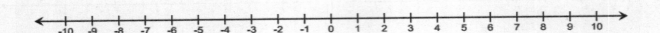

    c.   What is the distance between −6 and −10?

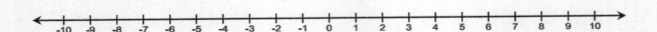

Example 1: Formula for the Distance Between Two Rational Numbers

Find the distance between −3 and 2.

Step 1: Start on an endpoint.

Step 2: Count the number of units from the endpoint you started on to the other endpoint.

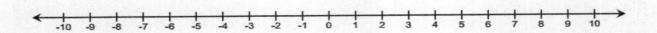

Using a formula, _____

> For two rational numbers p and q, the distance between p and q is $|p - q|$.

Distance is positive. Change in elevation or temperature may be positive or negative depending on whether it is increasing or decreasing (going up or down).

a. A hiker starts hiking at the beginning of a trail at a point which is 200 feet below sea level. He hikes to a location on the trail that is 580 feet above sea level and stops for lunch.

   i. What is the vertical distance between 200 feet below sea level and 580 feet above sea level?

   ii. How should we interpret 780 feet in the context of this problem?

b. After lunch, the hiker hiked back down the trail from the point of elevation, which is 580 feet above sea level, to the beginning of the trail, which is 200 feet below sea level.

   i. What is the vertical distance between 580 feet above sea level and 200 feet below sea level?

ii.   What is the change in elevation?

Exercise 3

The distance between a negative number and a positive number is $12\frac{1}{2}$. What are the numbers?

Exercise 4

Use the distance formula to find each answer. Support your answer using a number line diagram.

a.   Find the distance between -7 and -4.

b.   Find the change in temperature if the temperature rises from $-18°F$ to $15°F$ (use a vertical number line).

©2016 Great Minds. eureka-math.org
G7-M1M2-SE-B1-1.3.1-02.2016

c.   Would your answer for part (b) be different if the temperature dropped from 15°F to −18°F? Explain.

d.   Beryl is the first person to finish a 5K race and is standing 15 feet beyond the finish line. Another runner, Jeremy, is currently trying to finish the race and has approximately 14 feet before he reaches the finish line. What is the minimum possible distance between Beryl and Jeremy?

e.   What is the change in elevation from 140 feet above sea level to 40 feet below sea level? Explain.

Lesson Summary

- To find the distance between two rational numbers on a number line, you can count the number of units between the numbers.
- Using a formula, the distance between rational numbers, p and q, is $|p - q|$.
- Distance is always positive.
- Change may be positive or negative. For instance, there is a $-4°$ change when the temperature goes from $7°$ to $3°$.

Problem Set

1. $|-19 - 12|$

2. $|19 - (-12)|$

3. $|10 - (-43)|$

4. $|-10 - 43|$

5. $|-1 - (-16)|$

6. $|1 - 16|$

7. $|0 - (-9)|$

8. $|0 - 9|$

9. $|-14.5 - 13|$

10. $|14.5 - (-13)|$

11. Describe any patterns you see in the answers to the problems in the left- and right-hand columns. Why do you think this pattern exists?

EUREKA
MATH™

Lesson 7: Addition and Subtraction of Rational Numbers

Classwork

Exercise 1: Real-World Connection to Adding and Subtracting Rational Numbers

Suppose a seventh grader's birthday is today, and she is 12 years old. How old was she $3\frac{1}{2}$ years ago? Write an equation, and use a number line to model your answer.

Example 1: Representing Sums of Rational Numbers on a Number Line

a. Place the tail of the arrow on 12.

b. The length of the arrow is the absolute value of $-3\frac{1}{2}$, $\left|-3\frac{1}{2}\right| = 3\frac{1}{2}$.

c. The direction of the arrow is to the *left* since you are adding a negative number to 12.

Draw the number line model in the space below.

Exercise 2

Find the following sum using a number line diagram: $-2\frac{1}{2} + 5$.

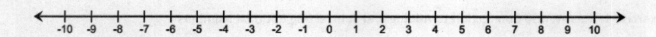

Example 2: Representing Differences of Rational Numbers on a Number Line

Find the following difference, and represent it on a number line: $1 - 2\frac{1}{4}$.

a.

Now follow the steps to represent the sum:

b.

c.

d.

Draw the number line model in the space below.

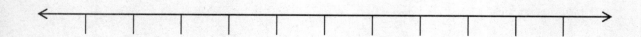

EUREKA
MATH™

©2016 Great Minds. eureka-math.org
G7-M1M2-SE-B1-1.3.1-02.2016

Exercise 3

Find the following difference, and represent it on a number line: $-5\frac{1}{2} - (-8)$.

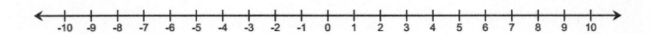

Exercise 4

Find the following sums and differences using a number line model.

  a. $-6 + 5\frac{1}{4}$

  b. $7 - (-0.9)$

  c. $2.5 + \left(-\frac{1}{2}\right)$

  d. $-\frac{1}{4} + 4$

e. $\frac{1}{2} - (-3)$

Exercise 5

Create an equation and number line diagram to model each answer.

a.   Samantha owes her father $7. She just got paid $5.50 for babysitting. If she gives that money to her dad, how much will she still owe him?

b.   At the start of a trip, a car's gas tank contains 12 gallons of gasoline. During the trip, the car consumes $10\frac{1}{8}$ gallons of gasoline. How much gasoline is left in the tank?

c.   A fish was swimming $3\frac{1}{2}$ feet below the water's surface at 7:00 a.m. Four hours later, the fish was at a depth that is $5\frac{1}{4}$ feet below where it was at 7:00 a.m. What rational number represents the position of the fish with respect to the water's surface at 11:00 a.m.?

©2016 Great Minds. eureka-math.org
G7-M1M2-SE-B1-1.3.1-02.2016

EUREKA MATH™

Lesson Summary

The rules for adding and subtracting integers apply to all rational numbers.

The sum of two rational numbers (e.g., $-1 + 4.3$) can be found on the number line by placing the tail of an arrow at -1 and locating the head of the arrow 4.3 units to the right to arrive at the sum, which is 3.3.

To model the difference of two rational numbers on a number line (e.g., $-5.7 - 3$), first rewrite the difference as a sum, $-5.7 + (-3)$, and then follow the steps for locating a sum. Place a single arrow with its tail at -5.7 and the head of the arrow 3 units to the left to arrive at -8.7.

Problem Set

Represent each of the following problems using both a number line diagram and an equation.

1. A bird that was perched atop a $15\frac{1}{2}$-foot tree dives down six feet to a branch below. How far above the ground is the bird's new location?

2. Mariah owed her grandfather $2.25 but was recently able to pay him back $1.50. How much does Mariah currently owe her grandfather?

3. Jake is hiking a trail that leads to the top of a canyon. The trail is 4.2 miles long, and Jake plans to stop for lunch after he completes 1.6 miles. How far from the top of the canyon will Jake be when he stops for lunch?

4. Sonji and her friend Rachel are competing in a running race. When Sonji is 0.4 miles from the finish line, she notices that her friend Rachel has fallen. If Sonji runs one-tenth of a mile back to help her friend, how far will she be from the finish line?

5. Mr. Henderson did not realize his checking account had a balance of $200 when he used his debit card for a $317.25 purchase. What is his checking account balance after the purchase?

6. If the temperature is $-3°F$ at $10{:}00$ p.m., and the temperature falls four degrees overnight, what is the resulting temperature?

This page intentionally left blank

Lesson 8: Applying the Properties of Operations to Add and Subtract Rational Numbers

Classwork

Example 1: The Opposite of a Sum is the Sum of its Opposites

Explain the meaning of "The opposite of a sum is the sum of its opposites." Use a specific math example.

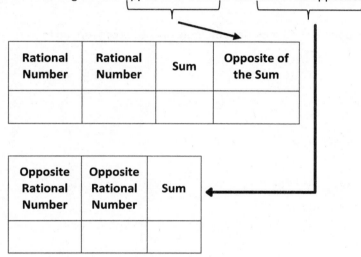

Rational Number	Rational Number	Sum	Opposite of the Sum

Opposite Rational Number	Opposite Rational Number	Sum

Exercise 1

Represent the following expression with a single rational number.

$$-2\frac{2}{5} + 3\frac{1}{4} - \frac{3}{5}$$

Example 2: A Mixed Number Is a Sum

Use the number line model shown below to explain and write the opposite of $2\frac{2}{5}$ as a sum of two rational numbers.

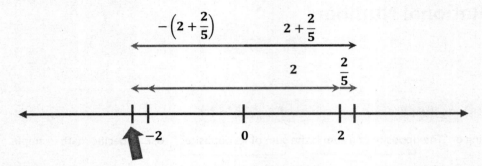

The opposite of a sum (top single arrow pointing left) and the sum of the opposites correspond to the same point on the number line.

Exercise 2

Rewrite each mixed number as the sum of two signed numbers.

a. $-9\frac{5}{8}$

b. $-2\frac{1}{2}$

c. $8\frac{11}{12}$

Exercise 3

Represent each sum as a mixed number.

a. $-1+\left(-\frac{5}{12}\right)$

b. $30+\frac{1}{8}$

c. $-17+\left(-\frac{1}{9}\right)$

Lesson 8: Applying the Properties of Operations to Add and Subtract Rational Numbers

©2016 Great Minds. eureka-math.org
G7-M1M2-SE-B1-1.3.1-02.2016

EUREKA MATH

Exercise 4

Mr. Mitchell lost 10 pounds over the summer by jogging each week. By winter, he had gained $5\frac{1}{8}$ pounds. Represent this situation with an expression involving signed numbers. What is the overall change in Mr. Mitchell's weight?

Exercise 5

Jamal is completing a math problem and represents the expression $-5\frac{5}{7} + 8 - 3\frac{2}{7}$ with a single rational number as shown in the steps below. Justify each of Jamal's steps. Then, show another way to solve the problem.

$$= -5\frac{5}{7} + 8 + \left(-3\frac{2}{7}\right)$$

$$= -5\frac{5}{7} + \left(-3\frac{2}{7}\right) + 8$$

$$= -5 + \left(-\frac{5}{7}\right) + (-3) + \left(-\frac{2}{7}\right) + 8$$

$$= -5 + \left(-\frac{5}{7}\right) + \left(-\frac{2}{7}\right) + (-3) + 8$$

$$= -5 + (-1) + (-3) + 8$$

$$= -6 + (-3) + 8$$

$$= (-9) + 8$$

$$= -1$$

Lesson Summary

- Use the properties of operations to add and subtract rational numbers more efficiently. For instance,

  $$-5\frac{2}{9} + 3.7 + 5\frac{2}{9} = \left(-5\frac{2}{9} + 5\frac{2}{9}\right) + 3.7 = 0 + 3.7 = 3.7.$$

- The opposite of a sum is the sum of its opposites as shown in the examples that follow:

  $$-4\frac{4}{7} = -4 + \left(-\frac{4}{7}\right)$$
  $$-(5 + 3) = -5 + (-3)$$

Problem Set

1. Represent each sum as a single rational number.

    a. $-14 + \left(-\frac{8}{9}\right)$ b. $7 + \frac{1}{9}$ c. $-3 + \left(-\frac{1}{6}\right)$

Rewrite each of the following to show that *the opposite of a sum is the sum of the opposites.* Problem 2 has been completed as an example.

2. $-(9 + 8) = -9 + (-8)$
    $-17 = -17$

3. $-\left(\frac{1}{4} + 6\right)$

4. $-\left(10 + (-6)\right)$

5. $-\left((-55) + \frac{1}{2}\right)$

Use your knowledge of rational numbers to answer the following questions.

6. Meghan said the opposite of the sum of -12 and 4 is 8. Do you agree? Why or why not?

7. Jolene lost her wallet at the mall. It had $10 in it. When she got home, her brother felt sorry for her and gave her $5.75. Represent this situation with an expression involving rational numbers. What is the overall change in the amount of money Jolene has?

8. Isaiah is completing a math problem and is at the last step: $25 - 28\frac{1}{5}$. What is the answer? Show your work.

     Lesson 8:   Applying the Properties of Operations to Add and Subtract Rational Numbers   **EUREKA MATH**

9. A number added to its opposite equals zero. What do you suppose is true about *a sum added to its opposite*?

Use the following examples to reach a conclusion. Express the answer to each example as a single rational number.

a. $(3 + 4) + (-3 + -4)$

b. $(-8 + 1) + (8 + (-1))$

c. $\left(-\frac{1}{2} + \left(-\frac{1}{4}\right)\right) + \left(\frac{1}{2} + \frac{1}{4}\right)$

This page intentionally left blank

Lesson 9: Applying the Properties of Operations to Add and Subtract Rational Numbers

Classwork

Exercise 1

Unscramble the cards, and show the steps in the correct order to arrive at the solution to $5\frac{2}{9} - \left(8.1 + 5\frac{2}{9}\right)$.

$$0 + (-8.1)$$

$$\left(5\frac{2}{9} + \left(-5\frac{2}{9}\right)\right) + (-8.1)$$

$$-8.1$$

$$5\frac{2}{9} + \left(-8.1 + \left(-5\frac{2}{9}\right)\right)$$

$$5\frac{2}{9} + \left(-5\frac{2}{9} + (-8.1)\right)$$

Examples 1–2

Represent each of the following expressions as one rational number. Show and explain your steps.

1. $4\frac{4}{7} - \left(4\frac{4}{7} - 10\right)$

2. $5 + \left(-4\frac{4}{7}\right)$

Lesson 9:   Applying the Properties of Operations to Add and Subtract Rational Numbers

©2016 Great Minds. eureka-math.org
G7-M1M2-SE-B1-1.3.1-02.2016

EUREKA MATH

Exercise 2: Team Work!

a. $-5.2 - (-3.1) + 5.2$

b. $32 + \left(-12\frac{7}{8}\right)$

c. $3\frac{1}{6} + 20.3 - \left(-5\frac{5}{6}\right)$

d. $\frac{16}{20} - (-1.8) - \frac{4}{5}$

Exercise 3

Explain, step by step, how to arrive at a single rational number to represent the following expression. Show both a written explanation and the related math work for each step.

$$-24 - \left(-\frac{1}{2}\right) - 12.5$$

EUREKA
MATH™

Lesson 9:   Applying the Properties of Operations to Add and Subtract Rational
              Numbers

S.57

©2016 Great Minds. eureka-math.org
G7-M1M2-SE-B1-1.3.1-02.2016

Lesson Summary

- Use the properties of operations to add and subtract rational numbers more efficiently. For instance,

$$-5\frac{2}{9} + 3.7 + 5\frac{2}{9} = \left(-5\frac{2}{9} + 5\frac{2}{9}\right) + 3.7 = 0 + 3.7 = 3.7.$$

- The opposite of a sum is the sum of its opposites as shown in the examples that follow:

$$-4\frac{4}{7} = -4 + \left(-\frac{4}{7}\right).$$

$$-(5 + 3) = -5 + (-3).$$

Problem Set

Show all steps taken to rewrite each of the following as a single rational number.

1. $80 + \left(-22\frac{4}{15}\right)$

2. $10 + \left(-3\frac{3}{8}\right)$

3. $\frac{1}{5} + 20.3 - \left(-5\frac{3}{5}\right)$

4. $\frac{11}{12} - (-10) - \frac{5}{6}$

5. Explain, step by step, how to arrive at a single rational number to represent the following expression. Show both a written explanation and the related math work for each step.

$$1 - \frac{3}{4} + \left(-12\frac{1}{4}\right)$$

Lesson 9:   Applying the Properties of Operations to Add and Subtract Rational
                          Numbers

©2016 Great Minds. eureka-math.org
G7-M1M2-SE-B1-1.3.1-02.2016

Lesson 10: Understanding Multiplication of Integers

Classwork

Exercise 1: Integer Game Revisited

In groups of four, play one round of the Integer Game (see Integer Game outline for directions).

Example 1: Product of a Positive Integer and a Negative Integer

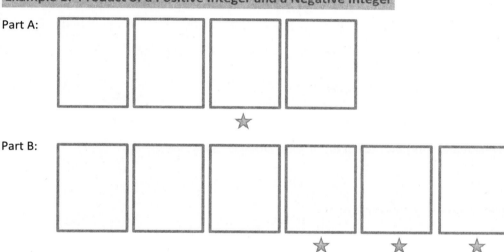

Part A:

Part B:

Use your cards from Part B to answer the questions below.

a. Write a product that describes the three matching cards.

b. Write an expression that represents how each of the ☆ cards changes your score.

c. Write an equation that relates these two expressions.

d. Write an integer that represents the total change to your score by the three ☆ cards.

e. Write an equation that relates the product and how it affects your score.

Part C:

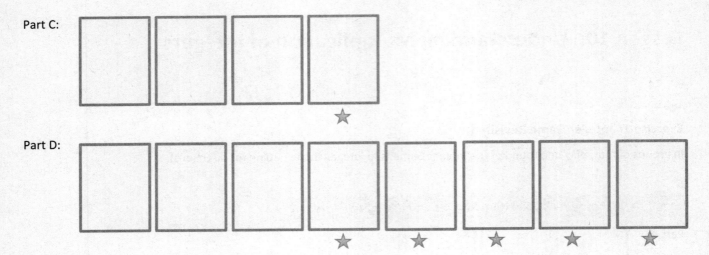

Part D:

Use your cards from Part D to answer the questions below.

f.   Write a product that describes the five matching cards.

g.   Write an expression that represents how each of the ☆ cards changes your score.

h.   Write an equation that relates these two expressions.

i.   Write an integer that represents the total change to your score by the five ☆ cards.

j.   Write an equation that relates the product and how it affects your score.

k.   Use the expression 5 × 4 to relate the multiplication of a positive valued card to addition.

l.   Use the expression 3 × (−5) to relate the multiplication of a negative valued card to addition.

Example 2: Product of a Negative Integer and a Positive Integer

a. If all of the 4's from the playing hand on the right are discarded, how will the score be affected? Model this using a product in an equation.

b. What three matching cards could be added to those pictured to get the same change in score? Model this using a product in an equation.

c. Seeing how each play affects the score, relate the products that you used to model them. What do you conclude about multiplying integers with opposite signs?

Example 3: Product of Two Negative Integers

a. If the matching cards from the playing hand on the right are discarded, how will this hand's score be affected? Model this using a product in an equation.

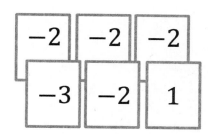

b. What four matching cards could be added to those pictured to get the same change in score? Model this using a product in an equation.

c. Seeing how each play affects the score, relate the products that you used to model them. What do you conclude about multiplying integers with the same sign?

d. Using the conclusions from Examples 2 and 3, what can we conclude about multiplying integers? Write a few examples.

EUREKA
MATH™

©2016 Great Minds. eureka-math.org
G7-M1M2-SE-B1-1.3.1-02.2016

Lesson Summary

Multiplying integers is repeated addition and can be modeled with the Integer Game. If $3 \times a$ corresponds to what happens to your score if you get three cards of value a, then $(-3) \times a$ corresponds to what happens to your score if you lose three cards of value a. Adding a number multiple times has the same effect as removing the opposite value the same number of times (e.g., $a \times b = (-a) \times (-b)$ and $a \times (-b) = (-a) \times b$).

Problem Set

1. Describe sets of two or more matching integer cards that satisfy the criteria in each part below:
   a. Cards increase the score by eight points.
   b. Cards decrease the score by 9 points.
   c. Removing cards that increase the score by 10 points.
   d. Positive cards that decrease the score by 18 points.

2. You have the integer cards shown at the right when your teacher tells you to choose a card to multiply four times. If your goal is to get your score as close to zero as possible, which card would you choose? Explain how your choice changes your score.

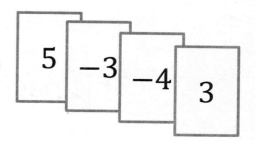

3. Sherry is playing the Integer Game and is given a chance to discard a set of matching cards. Sherry determines that if she discards one set of cards, her score will increase by 12. If she discards another set, then her score will decrease by eight. If her matching cards make up all six cards in her hand, what cards are in Sherry's hand? Are there any other possibilities?

This page intentionally left blank

Lesson 11: Develop Rules for Multiplying Signed Numbers

Classwork

Example 1: Extending Whole Number Multiplication to the Integers

Part A: Complete quadrants I and IV of the table below to show how sets of matching integer cards will affect a player's score in the Integer Game. For example, three 2s would increase a player's score by $0 + 2 + 2 + 2 = 6$ points.

Quadrant II Quadrant I

What does this quadrant represent?

_____

_____

_____

_____

What does this quadrant represent?

_____

_____

_____

_____

What does this quadrant represent?

_____

_____

_____

_____

What does this quadrant represent?

_____

_____

_____

_____

← Number of matching cards

Quadrant III ↑   Quadrant IV

Integer card values

(Table grid with values: middle column reading 5, 4, 3, 2, 1, then middle row with 1, 2, 3, 4, 5; then -1, -2, -3, -4, -5. The value 6 appears in Quadrant I.)

a. What patterns do you see in the right half of the table?

b. Enter the missing integers in the left side of the middle row, and describe what they represent.

Part B: Complete quadrant *II* of the table.

    c.   What relationships or patterns do you notice between the products (values) in quadrant *II* and the products (values) in quadrant *I*?

    d.   What relationships or patterns do you notice between the products (values) in quadrant *II* and the products (values) in quadrant *IV*?

    e.   Use what you know about the products (values) in quadrants *I*, *II*, and *IV* to describe what quadrant *III* will look like when its products (values) are entered.

Part C: Complete quadrant *III* of the table.

Refer to the completed table to help you answer the following questions:

    f.   Is it possible to know the sign of a product of two integers just by knowing in which quadrant each integer is located? Explain.

    g.   Which quadrants contain which values? Describe an Integer Game scenario represented in each quadrant.

©2016 Great Minds. eureka-math.org
G7-M1M2-SE-B1-1.3.1-02.2016

Exercise 1: Multiplication of Integers in the Real World

Generate real-world situations that can be modeled by each of the following multiplication problems. Use the Integer Game as a resource.

    a. -3×5

    b. $-6 \times (-3)$

    c. $4 \times (-7)$

©2016 Great Minds. eureka-math.org
G7-M1M2-SE-B1-1.3.1-02.2016

Lesson Summary

To multiply signed numbers, multiply the absolute values to get the absolute value of the product. The sign of the product is positive if the factors have the same sign and negative if they have opposite signs.

Problem Set

1. Complete the problems below. Then, answer the question that follows.

$3 \times 3 =$	$3 \times 2 =$	$3 \times 1 =$	$3 \times 0 =$	$3 \times (-1) =$	$3 \times (-2) =$
$2 \times 3 =$	$2 \times 2 =$	$2 \times 1 =$	$2 \times 0 =$	$2 \times (-1) =$	$2 \times (-2) =$
$1 \times 3 =$	$1 \times 2 =$	$1 \times 1 =$	$1 \times 0 =$	$1 \times (-1) =$	$1 \times (-2) =$
$0 \times 3 =$	$0 \times 2 =$	$0 \times 1 =$	$0 \times 0 =$	$0 \times (-1) =$	$0 \times (-2) =$
$-1 \times 3 =$	$-1 \times 2 =$	$-1 \times 1 =$	$-1 \times 0 =$	$-1 \times (-1) =$	$-1 \times (-2) =$
$-2 \times 3 =$	$-2 \times 2 =$	$-2 \times 1 =$	$-2 \times 0 =$	$-2 \times (-1) =$	$-2 \times (-2) =$
$-3 \times 3 =$	$-3 \times 2 =$	$-3 \times 1 =$	$-3 \times 0 =$	$-3 \times (-1) =$	$-3 \times (-2) =$

Which row shows the same pattern as the outlined column? Are the problems similar or different? Explain.

2. Explain why $(-4) \times (-5) = 20$. Use patterns, an example from the Integer Game, or the properties of operations to support your reasoning.

3. Each time that Samantha rides the commuter train, she spends $4 for her fare. Write an integer that represents the change in Samantha's money from riding the commuter train to and from work for 13 days. Explain your reasoning.

4. Write a real-world problem that can be modeled by $4 \times (-7)$.

Challenge:

5. Use properties to explain why for each integer a, $-a = -1 \times a$. (Hint: What does $\big(1 + (-1)\big) \times a$ equal? What is the additive inverse of a?)

Lesson 12: Division of Integers

Exercise 1: Recalling the Relationship Between Multiplication and Division

Record equations from Exercise 1 on the left.

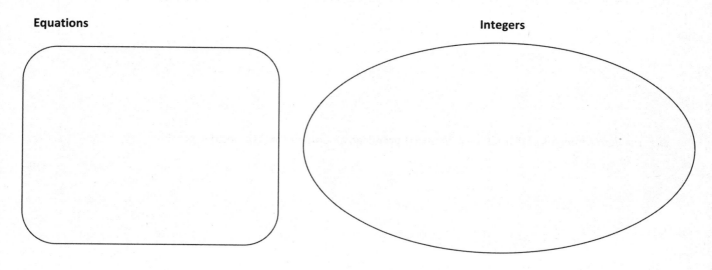

Example 1: Transitioning from Integer Multiplication Rules to Integer Division Rules

Record your group's number sentences in the space on the left below.

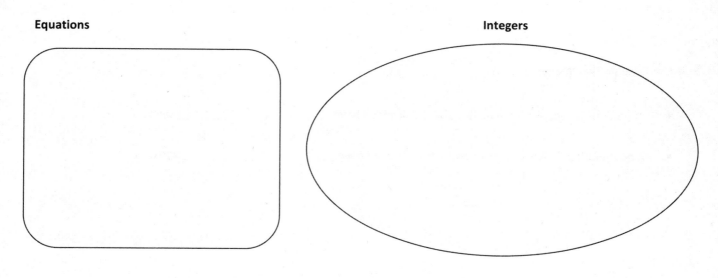

a. List examples of division problems that produced a quotient that is a negative number.

b. If the quotient is a negative number, what must be true about the signs of the dividend and divisor?

c. List your examples of division problems that produced a quotient that is a positive number.

d. If the quotient is a positive number, what must be true about the signs of the dividend and divisor?

Rules for Dividing Two Integers:

▪ A quotient is negative if the divisor and the dividend have _____ signs.

▪ A quotient is positive if the divisor and the dividend have _____ signs.

Exercise 2: Is the Quotient of Two Integers Always an Integer?

Is the quotient of two integers always an integer? Use the work space below to create quotients of integers. Answer the question, and use examples or a counterexample to support your claim.

Work Space:

Answer:

Exercise 3: Different Representation of the Same Quotient

Are the answers to the three quotients below the same or different? Why or why not?

    a. $-14 \div 7$

    b. $14 \div (-7)$

    c. $-(14 \div 7)$

Lesson Summary

The rules for dividing integers are similar to the rules for multiplying integers (when the divisor is not zero). The quotient is positive if the divisor and dividend have the same signs and negative if they have opposite signs.

The quotient of any two integers (with a nonzero divisor) will be a rational number. If p and q are integers, then

$$-\left(\frac{p}{q}\right) = \frac{-p}{q} = \frac{p}{-q}.$$

Problem Set

1. Find the missing values in each column.

Column A	Column B	Column C	Column D
$48 \div 4 =$	$24 \div 4 =$	$63 \div 7 =$	$21 \div 7 =$
$-48 \div (-4) =$	$-24 \div (-4) =$	$-63 \div (-7) =$	$-21 \div (-7) =$
$-48 \div 4 =$	$-24 \div 4 =$	$-63 \div 7 =$	$-21 \div 7 =$
$48 \div (-4) =$	$24 \div (-4) =$	$63 \div (-7) =$	$21 \div (-7) =$

2. Describe the pattern you see in each column's answers in Problem 1, relating it to the problems' divisors and dividends. Why is this so?

3. Describe the pattern you see between the answers for Columns A and B in Problem 1 (e.g., compare the first answer in Column A to the first answer in Column B; compare the second answer in Column A to the second answer in Column B). Why is this so?

4. Describe the pattern you see between the answers for Columns C and D in Problem 1. Why is this so?

EUREKA MATH™

Lesson 13: Converting Between Fractions and Decimals Using Equivalent Fractions

Classwork

Example 1: Representations of Rational Numbers in the Real World

Following the Opening Exercise and class discussion, describe why we need to know how to represent rational numbers in different ways.

Example 2: Using Place Values to Write (Terminating) Decimals as Equivalent Fractions

a.   What is the value of the number 2.25? How can this number be written as a fraction or mixed number?

b.   Rewrite the fraction in its simplest form showing all steps that you use.

c.   What is the value of the number 2.025? How can this number be written as a mixed number?

d.   Rewrite the fraction in its simplest form showing all steps that you use.

Exercise 1

Use place value to convert each terminating decimal to a fraction. Then rewrite each fraction in its simplest form.

    a.   0.218

    b.   0.16

    c.   2.72

    d.   0.0005

Example 3: Converting Fractions to Decimals—Fractions with Denominators Having Factors of only 2 or 5

    a.   What are *decimals*?

EUREKA
MATH™

©2016 Great Minds. eureka-math.org
G7-M1M2-SE-B1-1.3.1-02.2016

b. Use the meaning of *decimal* to relate decimal place values.

c. Write the number $\frac{3}{100}$ as a decimal. Describe your process.

d. Write the number $\frac{3}{20}$ as a decimal. Describe your process.

e. Write the number $\frac{10}{25}$ as a decimal. Describe your process.

f. Write the number $\frac{8}{40}$ as a decimal. Describe your process.

Exercise 2

Convert each fraction to a decimal using an equivalent fraction.

a. $\dfrac{3}{16} =$

b. $\dfrac{7}{5} =$

c. $\dfrac{11}{32} =$

d. $\dfrac{35}{50} =$

Lesson Summary

Any terminating decimal can be converted to a fraction using place value (e.g., 0.35 is thirty-five hundredths or $\frac{35}{100}$). A fraction whose denominator includes only factors of 2 and 5 can be converted to a decimal by writing the denominator as a power of ten.

Problem Set

1. Convert each terminating decimal to a fraction in its simplest form.
   a. 0.4
   b. 0.16
   c. 0.625
   d. 0.08
   e. 0.012

2. Convert each fraction or mixed number to a decimal using an equivalent fraction.
   a. $\frac{4}{5}$
   b. $\frac{3}{40}$
   c. $\frac{8}{200}$
   d. $3\frac{5}{16}$

3. Tanja is converting a fraction into a decimal by finding an equivalent fraction that has a power of 10 in the denominator. Sara looks at the last step in Tanja's work (shown below) and says that she cannot go any further. Is Sara correct? If she is, explain why. If Sara is incorrect, complete the remaining steps.

$$\frac{72}{480} = \frac{2^3 \cdot 3^2}{2^5 \cdot 3 \cdot 5}$$

This page intentionally left blank

Lesson 14: Converting Rational Numbers to Decimals Using Long Division

Classwork

Example 1: Can All Rational Numbers Be Written as Decimals?

a. Using the division button on your calculator, explore various quotients of integers 1 through 11. Record your fraction representations and their corresponding decimal representations in the space below.

b. What two types of decimals do you see?

Example 2: Decimal Representations of Rational Numbers

In the chart below, organize the fractions and their corresponding decimal representation listed in Example 1 according to their type of decimal.

What do these fractions have in common?   What do these fractions have in common?

Example 3: Converting Rational Numbers to Decimals Using Long Division

Use the long division algorithm to find the decimal value of $-\frac{3}{4}$.

Exercise 1

Convert each rational number to its decimal form using long division.

a. $-\frac{7}{8} =$

b. $\frac{3}{16} =$

©2016 Great Minds. eureka-math.org
G7-M1M2-SE-B1-1.3.1-02.2016

Example 4: Converting Rational Numbers to Decimals Using Long Division

Use long division to find the decimal representation of $\frac{1}{3}$.

Exercise 2

Calculate the decimal values of the fraction below using long division. Express your answers using bars over the shortest sequence of repeating digits.

a. $-\frac{4}{9}$

b. $-\frac{1}{11}$

c. $\frac{1}{7}$

d. $-\frac{5}{6}$

Example 5: Fractions Represent Terminating or Repeating Decimals

How do we determine whether the decimal representation of a quotient of two integers, with the divisor not equal to zero, will terminate or repeat?

Example 6: Using Rational Number Conversions in Problem Solving

a. Eric and four of his friends are taking a trip across the New York State Thruway. They decide to split the cost of tolls equally. If the total cost of tolls is $8, how much will each person have to pay?

b. Just before leaving on the trip, two of Eric's friends have a family emergency and cannot go.   What is each person's share of the $8 tolls now?

©2016 Great Minds. eureka-math.org
G7-M1M2-SE-B1-1.3.1-02.2016

Lesson Summary

The real world requires that we represent rational numbers in different ways depending on the context of a situation. All rational numbers can be represented as either terminating decimals or repeating decimals using the long division algorithm. We represent repeating decimals by placing a bar over the shortest sequence of repeating digits.

Problem Set

1. Convert each rational number into its decimal form.

$\frac{1}{6} = $ _____

$\frac{1}{3} = $ _____

$\frac{2}{3} = $ _____

$\frac{2}{6} = $ _____

$\frac{3}{6} = $ _____

$\frac{4}{6} = $ _____

$\frac{5}{6} = $ _____

$\frac{1}{9} = $ _____

$\frac{2}{9} = $ _____

$\frac{3}{9} = $ _____

$\frac{4}{9} = $ _____

$\frac{5}{9} = $ _____

$\frac{6}{9} = $ _____

$\frac{7}{9} = $ _____

$\frac{8}{9} = $ _____

One of these decimal representations is not like the others. Why?

EUREKA
MATH™

Lesson 14:   Converting Rational Numbers to Decimals Using Long Division

S.83

©2016 Great Minds. eureka-math.org
G7-M1M2-SE-B1-1.3.1-02.2016

Enrichment:

2. Chandler tells Aubrey that the decimal value of $-\frac{1}{17}$ is not a repeating decimal. Should Aubrey believe him? Explain.

3. Complete the quotients below without using a calculator, and answer the questions that follow.

   a. Convert each rational number in the table to its decimal equivalent.

$\frac{1}{11} =$	$\frac{2}{11} =$	$\frac{3}{11} =$	$\frac{4}{11} =$	$\frac{5}{11} =$
$\frac{6}{11} =$	$\frac{7}{11} =$	$\frac{8}{11} =$	$\frac{9}{11} =$	$\frac{10}{11} =$

   Do you see a pattern? Explain.

   b. Convert each rational number in the table to its decimal equivalent.

$\frac{0}{99} =$	$\frac{10}{99} =$	$\frac{20}{99} =$	$\frac{30}{99} =$	$\frac{45}{99} =$
$\frac{58}{99} =$	$\frac{62}{99} =$	$\frac{77}{99} =$	$\frac{81}{99} =$	$\frac{98}{99} =$

   Do you see a pattern? Explain.

   c. Can you find other rational numbers that follow similar patterns?

Lesson 14:   Converting Rational Numbers to Decimals Using Long Division

EUREKA MATH

©2016 Great Minds. eureka-math.org
G7-M1M2-SE-B1-1.3.1-02.2016

Lesson 15: Multiplication and Division of Rational Numbers

Classwork

Exercise 1

a. In the space below, create a word problem that involves integer multiplication. Write an equation to model the situation.

b. Now change the word problem by replacing the integers with non-integer rational numbers (fractions or decimals), and write the new equation.

c. Was the process used to solve the second problem different from the process used to solve the first? Explain.

d. The Rules for Multiplying Rational Numbers are the same as the Rules for Multiplying Integers:

   1. _____

   2. _____

   3. _____

Exercise 2

a. In one year, Melinda's parents spend $2,640.90 on cable and internet service. If they spend the same amount each month, what is the resulting monthly change in the family's income?

b. The Rules for Dividing Rational Numbers are the same as the Rules for Dividing Integers:

    1. _____

    2. _____

    3. _____

Exercise 3

Use the fundraiser chart to help answer the questions that follow.

Grimes Middle School Flower Fundraiser

Customer	Plant Type	Number of Plants	Price per Plant	Total	Paid? Yes or No
Tamara Jones	tulip	2	$4.25		No
Mrs. Wolff	daisy	1	$3.75	$ 3.75	Yes
Mr. Clark	geranium	5	$2.25		Yes
Susie (Jeremy's sister)	violet	1	$2.50	$ 2.50	Yes
Nana and Pop (Jeremy's grandparents)	daisy	4	$3.75	$15.00	No

Jeremy is selling plants for the school's fundraiser, and listed above is a chart from his fundraiser order form. Use the information in the chart to answer the following questions. Show your work, and represent the answer as a rational number; then, explain your answer in the context of the situation.

a.   If Tamara Jones writes a check to pay for the plants, what is the resulting change in her checking account balance?

Numerical Answer:

Explanation:

b.   Mr. Clark wants to pay for his order with a $20 bill, but Jeremy does not have change. Jeremy tells Mr. Clark he will give him the change later. How will this affect the total amount of money Jeremy collects? Explain. What rational number represents the change that must be made to the money Jeremy collects?

Numerical Answer:

Explanation:

c.   Jeremy's sister, Susie, borrowed the money from their mom to pay for her order. Their mother has agreed to deduct an equal amount of money from Susie's allowance each week for the next five weeks to repay the loan. What is the weekly change in Susie's allowance?

Numerical Answer:

Explanation:

d. Jeremy's grandparents want to change their order. They want to order three daisies and one geranium, instead of four daisies. How does this change affect the amount of their order? Explain how you arrived at your answer.

e. Jeremy approaches three people who do not want to buy any plants; however, they wish to donate some money for the fundraiser when Jeremy delivers the plants one week later. If the people promise to donate a total of $14.40, what will be the average cash donation?

f. Jeremy spends one week collecting orders. If 22 people purchase plants totaling $270, what is the average amount of Jeremy's sale?

Lesson Summary

The rules that apply for multiplying and dividing integers apply to rational numbers. We can use the products and quotients of rational numbers to describe real-world situations.

Problem Set

1. At lunch time, Benjamin often borrows money from his friends to buy snacks in the school cafeteria. Benjamin borrowed $0.75 from his friend Clyde five days last week to buy ice cream bars. Represent the amount Benjamin borrowed as the product of two rational numbers; then, determine how much Benjamin owed his friend last week.

2. Monica regularly records her favorite television show. Each episode of the show requires 3.5% of the total capacity of her video recorder. Her recorder currently has 62% of its total memory free. If Monica records all five episodes this week, how much space will be left on her video recorder?

For Problems 3–5, find at least two possible sets of values that will work for each problem.

3. Fill in the blanks with two rational numbers (other than 1 and −1). ___ × $\left(-\frac{1}{2}\right)$ × ___ = −20
   What must be true about the relationship between the two numbers you chose?

4. Fill in the blanks with two rational numbers (other than 1 and −1). −5.6 × 100 ÷ 80 × ___ × ___ = 700
   What must be true about the relationship between the two numbers you chose?

5. Fill in the blanks with two rational numbers. ___ × ___ = −0.75
   What must be true about the relationship between the two numbers you chose?

For Problems 6–8, create word problems that can be represented by each expression, and then represent each product or quotient as a single rational number.

6. 8 × (−0.25)

7. −6 ÷ $\left(1\frac{1}{3}\right)$

8. $-\frac{1}{2}$ × 12

This page intentionally left blank

Lesson 16: Applying the Properties of Operations to Multiply and Divide Rational Numbers

Classwork

Example 1: Using the Commutative and Associative Properties to Efficiently Multiply Rational Numbers

a. Evaluate the expression below.

$$-6 \times 2 \times (-2) \times (-5) \times (-3)$$

b. What types of strategies were used to evaluate the expressions?

c. Can you identify the benefits of choosing one strategy versus another?

d. What is the sign of the product, and how was the sign determined?

Exercise 1

Find an efficient strategy to evaluate the expression and complete the necessary work.

$$-1 \times (-3) \times 10 \times (-2) \times 2$$

Exercise 2

Find an efficient strategy to evaluate the expression and complete the necessary work.

$$4 \times \frac{1}{3} \times (-8) \times 9 \times \left(-\frac{1}{2}\right)$$

Exercise 3

What terms did you combine first and why?

©2016 Great Minds. eureka-math.org
G7-M1M2-SE-B1-1.3.1-02.2016

EUREKA MATH

Exercise 4

Refer to the example and exercises. Do you see an easy way to determine the sign of the product first?

Example 2: Using the Distributive Property to Multiply Rational Numbers

Rewrite the mixed number as a sum; then, multiply using the distributive property.

$$-6 \times \left(5\frac{1}{3}\right)$$

Exercise 5

Multiply the expression using the distributive property.

$$9 \times \left(-3\frac{1}{2}\right)$$

Example 3: Using the Distributive Property to Multiply Rational Numbers

Evaluate using the distributive property.

$$16 \times \left(-\frac{3}{8}\right) + 16 \times \frac{1}{4}$$

Example 4: Using the Multiplicative Inverse to Rewrite Division as Multiplication

Rewrite the expression as only multiplication and evaluate.

$$1 \div \frac{2}{3} \times (-8) \times 3 \div \left(-\frac{1}{2}\right)$$

Exercise 6

$$4.2 \times \left(-\frac{1}{3}\right) \div \frac{1}{6} \times (-10)$$

EUREKA
MATH™

Lesson Summary

Multiplying and dividing using the strict order of the operations in an expression is not always efficient. The properties of multiplication allow us to manipulate the expression by rearranging and regrouping factors that are easier to compute (like grouping factors 2 and 5 to get 10).

Where division is involved, we can easily rewrite the division by a number as multiplication by its reciprocal, and then use the properties of multiplication.

If an expression is only a product of factors, then the sign of its value is easily determined by the number of negative factors: the sign is positive if there are an even number of negative factors and negative if there is an odd number of factors.

Problem Set

1. Evaluate the expression $-2.2 \times (-2) \div \left(-\frac{1}{4}\right) \times 5$

   a. Using the order of operations only.

   b. Using the properties and methods used in Lesson 16.

   c. If you were asked to evaluate another expression, which method would you use, (a) or (b), and why?

2. Evaluate the expressions using the distributive property.

   a. $\left(2\frac{1}{4}\right) \times (-8)$

   b. $\frac{2}{3}(-7) + \frac{2}{3}(-5)$

3. Mia evaluated the expression below but got an incorrect answer. Find Mia's error(s), find the correct value of the expression, and explain how Mia could have avoided her error(s).

   $0.38 \times 3 \div \left(-\frac{1}{20}\right) \times 5 \div (-8)$

   $0.38 \times 5 \times \left(\frac{1}{20}\right) \times 3 \times (-8)$

   $0.38 \times \left(\frac{1}{4}\right) \times 3 \times (-8)$

   $0.38 \times \left(\frac{1}{4}\right) \times (-24)$

   $0.38 \times (-6)$

   -2.28

This page intentionally left blank

Lesson 17: Comparing Tape Diagram Solutions to Algebraic Solutions

Classwork

Opening Exercise

For his birthday, Zack and three of his friends went to a movie. They each got a ticket for $8.00 and the same snack from the concession stand. If Zack's mom paid $48 for the group's tickets and snacks, how much did each snack cost?

The equation $4(s + 8) = 48$ represents the situation when s represents the cost, in dollars, of one snack.

Exploratory Challenge: Expenses on Your Family Vacation

John and Ag are summarizing some of the expenses of their family vacation for themselves and their three children, Louie, Missy, and Bonnie. Write an algebraic equation, create a model to determine how much each item will cost using all of the given information, and answer the questions that follow.

Expenses:

Car and insurance fees: $400	Airfare and insurance fees: $875	Motel and tax: $400
Baseball game and hats: $103.83	Movies for one day: $75	Soda and pizza: $37.95
	Sandals and T-shirts: $120	

Your Group's Scenario Solution:

©2016 Great Minds. eureka-math.org
G7-M1M2-SE-B1-1.3.1-02.2016

After collaborating with all of the groups, summarize the findings in the table below.

Cost of Evening Movie	
Cost of 1 Slice of Pizza	
Cost of the Admission Ticket to the Baseball Game	
Cost of 1 T-Shirt	
Cost of 1 Airplane Ticket	
Daily Cost for Car Rental	
Nightly Charge for Motel	

Using the results, determine the cost of the following:

1.   A slice of pizza, 1 plane ticket, 2 nights in the motel, and 1 evening movie.

2.   One T-shirt, 1 ticket to the baseball game, and 1 day of the rental car.

Exercise

The cost of a babysitting service on a cruise is $10 for the first hour and $12 for each additional hour. If the total cost of babysitting baby Aaron was $58, how many hours was Aaron at the sitter?

Lesson Summary

Tape diagrams can be used to model and identify the sequence of operations to find a solution algebraically.

The goal in solving equations algebraically is to isolate the variable.

The process of doing this requires *undoing* addition or subtraction to obtain a 0 and *undoing* multiplication or division to obtain a 1. The additive inverse and multiplicative inverse properties are applied to get the 0 (the additive identity) and 1 (the multiplicative identity).

The addition and multiplication properties of equality are applied because in an equation, $A = B$, when a number is added or multiplied to both sides, the resulting sum or product remains equal.

Problem Set

1. A taxi cab in Myrtle Beach charges $2 per mile and $1 for every person. If a taxi cab ride for two people costs $12, how far did the taxi cab travel?

2. Heather works as a waitress at her family's restaurant. She works 2 hours every morning during the breakfast shift and returns to work each evening for the dinner shift. In the last four days, she worked 28 hours. If Heather works the same number of hours every evening, how many hours did she work during each dinner shift?

3. Jillian exercises 5 times a week. She runs 3 miles each morning and bikes in the evening. If she exercises a total of 30 miles for the week, how many miles does she bike each evening?

4. Marc eats an egg sandwich for breakfast and a big burger for lunch every day. The egg sandwich has 250 calories. If Marc has 5,250 calories for breakfast and lunch for the week in total, how many calories are in one big burger?

5. Jackie won tickets playing the bowling game at the local arcade. The first time, she won 60 tickets. The second time, she won a bonus, which was 4 times the number of tickets of the original second prize. Altogether she won 200 tickets. How many tickets was the original second prize?

This page intentionally left blank

Lesson 18: Writing, Evaluating, and Finding Equivalent Expressions with Rational Numbers

Classwork

Exercise 1

John's father asked him to compare several different cell phone plans and identify which plan will be the least expensive for the family. Each phone company charges a monthly fee, but this fee does not cover any services: phone lines, texting, or internet access. Use the information contained in the table below to answer the following questions.

Cell Phone Plans

Name of Plan	Monthly Fee (Includes 1,500 shared minutes)	Price per Phone Line x	Price per line for Unlimited Texting y	Price per line for Internet Access z
Company A	$70	$20	$15	$15
Company B	$90	$15	$10	$20
Company C	$200	$10	included in monthly fee	included in monthly fee

All members of the family may not want identical plans; therefore, we will let x represent the number of phone lines, y represent the number of phone lines with unlimited texting, and z represent the number of phone lines with internet access.

Expression

Company A _____

Company B _____

Company C _____

Using the expressions above, find the cost to the family of each company's phone plan if:

a. Four people want a phone line, four people want unlimited texting, and the family needs two internet lines.

Company A	Company B	Company C

Which cell phone company should John's family use? Why?

b. Four people want a phone line, four people want unlimited texting, and all four people want internet lines.

Company A	Company B	Company C

Which cell phone company should John's family use? Why?

Lesson 18:   Writing, Evaluating, and Finding Equivalent Expressions with Rational
Numbers

©2016 Great Minds. eureka-math.org
G7-M1M2-SE-B1-1.3.1-02.2016

EUREKA
MATH™

c.   Two people want a phone line, two people want unlimited texting, and the family needs two internet lines.

Company A	Company B	Company C

Which cell phone company should John's family use? Why?

Exercise 2

Three friends went to the movies. Each purchased a medium-sized popcorn for p dollars and a small soft drink for s dollars.

   a.   Write the expression that represents the total amount of money (in dollars) the three friends spent at the concession stand.

   b.   If the concession stand charges $6.50 for a medium-sized popcorn and $4.00 for a small soft drink, how much did the three friends spend on their refreshments altogether?

Exercise 3

Complete the table below by writing equivalent expressions to the given expression and evaluating each expression with the given values.

Equivalent Expressions			
EXAMPLE: Evaluate $x = 2,$ $y = -1$	$4(x + 2y)$ $4(2 + 2(-1))$ $4(0)$ 0	$4x + 8y$ $4(2) + 8(-1)$ $8 + (-8)$ 0	$4x + 4y + 4y$ $4(2) + 4(-1) + 4(-1)$ $8 + (-4) + (-4)$ 0
1. Evaluate $y = 1$	$5(3 - 4y)$		
2. Evaluate $x = 5,$ $y = -2$	$-3x + 12y$		

Lesson 18: Writing, Evaluating, and Finding Equivalent Expressions with Rational Numbers

EUREKA MATH™

3. Evaluate $x = -\dfrac{1}{2},$ $y = 1$			$-2x + 10x - 6y$

©2016 Great Minds. eureka-math.org
G7-M1M2-SE-B1-1.3.1-02.2016

> **Lesson Summary**
>
> - An expression is a number or a letter, which can be raised to a whole number exponent. An expression can be a product whose factors are any one of the entities described above. An expression can also be the sum or difference of the products described above.
>
> - To evaluate an expression, replace each variable with its corresponding numerical value. Using order of operations, the expression can be written as a single numerical value.
>
> - When numbers are substituted into all the letters in an expression and the results are the same, then the expressions are equivalent.

Problem Set

1. Sally is paid a fixed amount of money to walk her neighbor's dog every day after school. When she is paid each month, she puts aside $20 to spend and saves the remaining amount. Write an expression that represents the amount Sally will save in 6 months if she earns m dollars each month. If Sally is paid $65 each month, how much will she save in 6 months?

2. A football team scored 3 touchdowns, 3 extra points, and 4 field goals.

    a. Write an expression to represent the total points the football team scored.

    b. Write another expression that is equivalent to the one written above.

    c. If each touchdown is worth 6 points, each extra point is 1 point, and each field goal is 3 points, how many total points did the team score?

3. Write three other expressions that are equivalent to $8x - 12$.

Lesson 18:   Writing, Evaluating, and Finding Equivalent Expressions with Rational Numbers

©2016 Great Minds. eureka-math.org
G7-M1M2-SE-B1-1.3.1-02.2016

4. Profit is defined as earnings less expenses (earnings − expenses). At the local hot-air balloon festival, the Ma & Pops Ice Cream Truck sells ice cream pops, which cost them $0.75 each, but are sold for $2 each. They also paid $50 to the festival's organizers for a vendor permit. The table below shows the earnings, expenses, and profit earned when 50, 75, and 100 ice cream pops were sold at the festival.

Number of Pops Sold	Earnings	Expenses	Profit
50	$50(2) = 100$	$50(0.75) + 50$ $37.5 + 50 = 87.5$	$100 − 87.5 = 12.50$
75	$75(2) = 150$	$75(0.75) + 50$ $56.25 + 50 = 106.25$	$150 − 106.25 = 43.75$
100	$100(2) = 200$	$100(0.75) + 50$ $75 + 50 = 125$	$200 − 125 = 75$

a. Write an expression that represents the profit (in dollars) Ma & Pops earned by selling ice cream pops at the festival.

b. Write an equivalent expression.

c. How much of a profit did Ma & Pops Ice Cream Truck make if it sold 20 ice cream pops? What does this mean? Explain why this might be the case.

d. How much of a profit did Ma & Pops Ice Cream Truck make if it sold 75 ice cream pops? What does this mean? Explain why this might be the case.

This page intentionally left blank

Lesson 19: Writing, Evaluating, and Finding Equivalent Expressions with Rational Numbers

Classwork

Fill in the 9 spaces with one expression from the list below. Use one expression per space. You will use 9 of the expressions:

$12 - 4x$

$8x + 4 - 12x$

$8\left(\dfrac{1}{2}x - 2\right)$

$12 - 6x + 2x$

$-4x + 4$

$x - 2 + 2x - 4$

$4x - 12$

$4(x - 4)$

$3(x - 2)$

$0.1(40x) - \dfrac{1}{2}(24)$

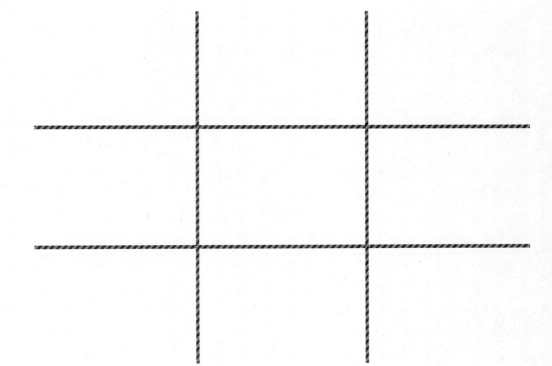

Example 2

Original Price (100%)	Discount Amount (20% Off)	New Price (Pay 80%)	Expression
100			
50			
28			
14.50			
x			

Lesson 19:   Writing, Evaluating, and Finding Equivalent Expressions with Rational Numbers

©2016 Great Minds. eureka-math.org
G7-M1M2-SE-B1-1.3.1-02.2016

EUREKA MATH

Example 3

An item that has an original price of x dollars is discounted 33%.

    a.   Write an expression that represents the amount of the discount.

    b.   Write two equivalent expressions that represent the new, discounted price.

    c.   Use one of your expressions to calculate the new, discounted price if the original price was $56.

    d.   How would the expressions you created in parts (a) and (b) have to change if the item's price had increased by 33% instead of decreased by 33%?

Example 4

Original Price (100%)	Discount (20%) off	Amount Pay (pay 80%)	Expression	New Price	Sales Tax (8%)	Overall Cost	Expression
100	20	80	$100 - 100(0.20) = 100(0.80)$				
50	10	40	$50 - 50(0.20) = 50(0.80)$				
28	5.60	22.40	$28 - 28(0.20) = 28(0.80)$				
14.50	2.90	11.60	$14.50 - 14.50(0.20)$ or $14.50(0.80)$				
x	$0.20x$	$x - 0.20x$	$x - 0.20x$ or $0.80x$				

Lesson 19: Writing, Evaluating, and Finding Equivalent Expressions with Rational Numbers

EUREKA MATH

Lesson Summary

- Two expressions are equivalent if they yield the same number for every substitution of numbers for the letters in each expression.
- The expression that allows us to find the cost of an item after the discount has been taken and the sales tax has been added is written by representing the discount price added to the discount price multiplied by the sales tax rate.

Problem Set

Solve the following problems. If necessary, round to the nearest penny.

1. A family of 12 went to the local Italian restaurant for dinner. Every family member ordered a drink and meal, 3 ordered an appetizer, and 6 people ordered cake for dessert.

   a. Write an expression that can be used to figure out the cost of the bill. Include the definitions for the variables the server used.

   b. The waitress wrote on her ordering pad the following expression: $3(4d + 4m + a + 2c)$. Was she correct? Explain why or why not.

   c. What is the cost of the bill if a drink costs $3, a meal costs $20, an appetizer costs $5.50, and a slice of cake costs $3.75?

   d. Suppose the family had a 10% discount coupon for the entire check and then left an 18% tip. What is the total?

2. Sally designs web pages for customers. She charges $135.50 per web page; however, she must pay a monthly rental fee of $650 for her office. Write an expression to determine her take-home pay after expenses. If Sally designed 5 web pages last month, what was her take-home pay after expenses?

3. While shopping, Megan and her friend Rylie find a pair of boots on sale for 25% off the original price. Megan calculates the final cost of the boots by first deducting the 25% and then adding the 6% sales tax. Rylie thinks Megan will pay less if she pays the 6% sales tax first and then takes the 25% discount.

   a. Write an expression to represent each girl's scenario if the original price of the boots was x dollars.

   b. Evaluate each expression if the boots originally cost $200.

   c. Who was right? Explain how you know.

   d. Explain how both girls' expressions are equivalent.

This page intentionally left blank

Lesson 20: Investments—Performing Operations with Rational Numbers

Mathematical Modeling Exercise: College Investments

Justin and Adrienne deposited $20,000 into an investment account for 5 years. They hoped the money invested and the money made on their investment would amount to at least $30,000 to help pay for their daughter's college tuition and expenses. The account they chose has several benefits and fees associated with it. Every 6 months, a summary statement is sent to Justin and Adrienne. The statement includes the amount of money either gained or lost. Below are semiannual (twice a year) statements for a period of 5 years. In addition to the statements, the following information is needed to complete the task:

- For every statement, there is an administrative fee of $15 to cover costs such as secretarial work, office supplies, and postage.
- If there is a withdrawal made, a broker's fee is deducted from the account. The amount of the broker's fee is 2% of the transaction amount.

TASK: Using the above information, semiannual statements, register, and beginning balance, do the following:

1. Record the beginning balance and all transactions from the account statements into the register.
2. Determine the annual gain or loss as well as the overall 5-year gain or loss.
3. Determine if there is enough money in the account after 5 years to cover $30,000 of college expenses for Justin and Adrienne's daughter. Write a summary to defend your answer. Be sure to indicate how much money is in excess, or the shortage that exists.
4. Answer the related questions that follow.

College Investment Fund Semi-Annual Statement

January 1, 2008 – June 30, 2008

Investment Gain/(Loss):   700.00

College Investment Fund Semi-Annual Statement

July 1, 2008 – December 31, 2008

Investment Gain/(Loss):   754.38

College Investment Fund Semi-Annual Statement

January 1, 2009 – June 30, 2009

Investment Gain/(Loss):   (49.88)

College Investment Fund Semi-Annual Statement

July 1, 2009 – December 31, 2009

Withdrawal: 500.00
Investment Gain/(Loss: (17.41)

College Investment Fund Semi-Annual Statement

January 1, 2010 – June 30, 2010

Investment Gain/(Loss):   676.93

College Investment Fund Semi-Annual Statement

July 1, 2010 – December 31, 2010

Investment Gain/(Loss):   759.45

College Investment Fund Semi-Annual Statement

January 1, 2011 – June 30, 2011

Deposit: 1,500.00
Investment Gain/(Loss):   880.09

College Investment Fund Semi-Annual Statement

July 1, 2011 – December 31, 2011

Investment Gain/(Loss):   922.99

College Investment Fund Semi-Annual Statement

January 1, 2012 – June 30, 2012

Deposit: 800.00
Investment Gain/(Loss):   942.33

College Investment Fund Semi-Annual Statement

July 1, 2012 – December 31, 2012

Investment Gain/(Loss):   909.71

EUREKA MATH

5. Register

DATE	DESCRIPTION OF TRANSACTION	WITHDRAWAL	DEPOSIT	BALANCE	EXPRESSION
	Beginning Balance	---	---	$20,000.00	$20,000.00
Jan. – June: 2008					
July – Dec.: 2008					
Jan. – June: 2009					
July – Dec.: 2009					
Jan. – June: 2010					
July – Dec.: 2010					
Jan. – June: 2011					
July – Dec.: 2011					
Jan. – June: 2012					
July – Dec.: 2012					

6. Annual Gain/Loss Summary

Year	Total Gain/(Loss)	Numerical Expression
2008		
2009		
2010		
2011		
2012		
5-Year Gain/Loss		

7. Summary

Lesson 20:   Investments—Performing Operations with Rational Numbers

EUREKA MATH™

8. Related Questions

   a. For the first half of 2009, there was a $700 gain on the initial investment of $20,000. Represent the gain as a percentage of the initial investment.

   b. Based on the gains and losses on their investment during this 5-year period, over what period of time was their investment not doing well? How do you know? What factors might contribute to this?

   c. In math class, Jaheim and Frank were working on finding the total amount of the investment after 5 years. As a final step, Jaheim subtracted $150 for administrative fees from the balance he arrived at after adding in all the deposits and subtracting out the one withdrawal and broker's fee. For every semiannual statement, Frank subtracted $15 from the account balance for the administrative fee. Both boys arrived at the same ending 5-year balance. How is this possible? Explain.

   d. Based on the past statements for their investment account, predict what activity you might expect to see on Adrienne and Justin's January–June 2013 account statement. Then record it in the register to arrive at the balance as of June 30, 2013.

   e. Using the answer from part (d), if their daughter's college bill is due in September 2013 of, how much money do you estimate will be in their investment account at the end of August 2013 before the college bill is paid? Support your answer.

Exercise

Below is a transaction log of a business entertainment account. The transactions are completed and the ending balance in the account is $525.55. Determine the beginning balance.

DATE	DESCRIPTION OF TRANSACTION	PAYMENT	DEPOSIT	BALANCE
	Beginning Balance	---	---	
12/1/10	Bargain Electronic (i-Pod)	199.99		
12/5/10	Lenny's Drive-Up (Gift Certificate)	75.00		
12/7/10	Check from Customer: Reynolds		200.00	
12/15/10	Pasta House (Dinner)	285.00		
12/20/10	Refund from Clear's Play House		150.00	
12/22/10	Gaffney's Tree Nursery	65.48		525.55

EUREKA
MATH™

Problem Set

1. You are planning a fundraiser for your student council. The fundraiser is a Glow in the Dark Dance. Solve each entry below, and complete the transaction log to determine the ending balance in the student account.

    a. The cost of admission to the dance is $7 per person, and all tickets were sold on November 1. Write an expression to represent the total amount of money collected for admission. Evaluate the expression if 250 people attended the dance.

    b. The following expenses were necessary for the dance, and checks were written to each company.

        - DJ for the dance—*Music Madness DJ* costs $200 and paid for on November 3.
        - Glow sticks from *Glow World, Inc.* for the first 100 entrants. Cost of glow sticks was $0.75 each plus 8% sales tax and bought on November 4.

        Complete the transaction log below based on this information

DATE	DESCRIPTION OF TRANSACTION	PAYMENT	DEPOSIT	BALANCE
	Beginning Balance	---	---	1,243.56

    c. Write a numerical expression to determine the cost of the glow sticks.

    Analyze the results.

    d. Write an algebraic expression to represent the profit earned from the fundraiser. (Profit is the amount of money collected in admissions minus all expenses.)

    e. Evaluate the expression to determine the profit if 250 people attended the dance. Use the variable p to represent the number of people attending the dance (from part (a)).

    f. Using the transaction log above, what was the amount of the profit earned?

2. The register below shows a series of transactions made to an investment account. Vinnie and Anthony both completed the register in hopes of finding the beginning balance. As you can see, they do not get the same answer. Who was correct? What mistake did the other person make? What was the monthly gain or loss?

Original Register

DATE	DESCRIPTION OF TRANSACTION	PAYMENT	DEPOSIT	BALANCE
	Beginning Balance	---	---	
3/1/11	Broker's Fee	250.00		
3/10/11	Loan Withdrawal	895.22		
3/15/11	Refund – Misc. Fee		50.00	
3/31/11	Investment Results		2,012.22	18,917.00

Vinnie's Work

DATE	DESCRIPTION OF TRANSACTION	PAYMENT	DEPOSIT	BALANCE
	Beginning Balance	---	---	18,000.00
3/1/11	Broker's Fee	250.00		17,750.00
3/10/11	Loan Withdrawal	895.22		16,854.78
3/15/11	Refund – Misc. Fee		50.00	16,904.78
3/31/11	Investment Results		2,012.22	18,917.00

Anthony's Work

DATE	DESCRIPTION OF TRANSACTION	PAYMENT	DEPOSIT	BALANCE
	Beginning Balance	---	---	19,834.00
3/1/11	Broker's Fee	250.00		20,084.00
3/10/11	Loan Withdrawal	895.22		20,979.22
3/15/11	Refund – Misc. Fee		50.00	20,929.22
3/31/11	Investment Results		2,012.22	18,917.00

©2016 Great Minds. eureka-math.org
G7-M1M2-SE-B1-1.3.1-02.2016

Lesson 21: If–Then Moves with Integer Number Cards

Classwork

Exploratory Challenge: Integer Game Revisited

Let's investigate what happens if a card is added or removed from a hand of integers.

My cards:

My score:

Event 1

My new score:

Conclusion:

EUREKA
MATH™

Lesson 21:   If-Then Moves with Integer Number Cards

S.125

©2016 Great Minds. eureka-math.org
G7-M1M2-SE-B1-1.3.1-02.2016

Event 2

My new score:

Conclusion:

Event 3

My new score:

Expression:

Conclusion:

EUREKA
MATH™

Event 4

Expression:

Conclusion:

Exercises

1. The table below shows two hands from the Integer Game and a series of changes that occurred to each hand. Part of the table is completed for you. Complete the remaining part of the table; then summarize the results.

	Hand 1	Result	Hand 2	Result
Original	$1 + (-4) + 2$		$0 + 5 + (-6)$	
Add 4	$1 + (-4) + 2 + 4$			
Subtract 1	$1 + (-4) + 2 + 4 - 1$			
Multiply by 3				
Divide by 2				

2. Complete the table below using the multiplication property of equality.

	Original expression and result	Equivalent expression and result
	$3 + (-5) =$	
Multiply both expressions by -3		
Write a conclusion using if–then		

©2016 Great Minds. eureka-math.org
G7-M1M2-SE-B1-1.3.1-02.2016

Lesson Summary

- If a number sentence is true, and the same number is added to both sides of the equation, then the resulting number sentence is true. *(addition property of equality)*
- If a number sentence is true, and the same number is subtracted from both sides of the equation, then the resulting number sentence is true. *(subtraction property of equality)*
- If a number sentence is true, and both sides of the equation are multiplied by the same number, then the resulting number sentence is true. *(multiplication property of equality)*
- If a number sentence is true, and both sides of the equation are divided by the same nonzero number, then the resulting number sentence is true. *(division property of equality)*

Problem Set

1. Evaluate the following numerical expressions.

   a. $2 + (-3) + 7$

   b. $-4 - 1$

   c. $-\frac{5}{2} \times 2$

   d. $-10 \div 2 + 3$

   e. $\left(\frac{1}{2}\right)(8) + 2$

   f. $3 + (-4) - 1$

2. Which expressions from Exercise 1 are equal?

3. If two of the equivalent expressions from Exercise 1 are divided by 3, write an if–then statement using the properties of equality.

4. Write an if–then statement if -3 is multiplied to the following equation: $-1 - 3 = -4$.

5. Simplify the expression. $5 + 6 - 5 + 4 + 7 - 3 + 6 - 3$

   Using the expression, write an equation.

   Rewrite the equation if 5 is added to both expressions.

   Write an if–then statement using the properties of equality.

This page intentionally left blank

Lesson 22: Solving Equations Using Algebra

Classwork

In this lesson, you will transition from solving equations using tape diagrams to solving equations algebraically by *making zero* (using the additive inverse) and *making one* (using the multiplicative inverse). Justify your work by identifying which algebraic property you used for each step in solving the problems. Explain your work by writing out how you solved the equations step by step and relate each step to those used with a tape diagram.

Example 1: Yoshiro's New Puppy

Yoshiro has a new puppy. She decides to create an enclosure for her puppy in her backyard. The enclosure is in the shape of a hexagon (six-sided polygon) with one pair of opposite sides running the same distance along the length of two parallel flower beds. There are two boundaries at one end of the flower beds that are 10 ft. and 12 ft., respectively, and at the other end, the two boundaries are 15 ft. and 20 ft., respectively. If the perimeter of the enclosure is 137 ft., what is the length of each side that runs along the flower bed?

Example 2: Swim Practice

Jenny is on the local swim team for the summer and has swim practice four days per week. The schedule is the same each day. The team swims in the morning and then again for 2 hours in the evening. If she swims 12 hours per week, how long does she swim each morning?

Exercises

Solve each equation algebraically using if–then statements to justify each step.

1. $5x + 4 = 19$

2. $15x + 14 = 19$

3.   Claire's mom found a very good price on a large computer monitor. She paid $325 for a monitor that was only $65 more than half the original price. What was the original price?

4. $2(x + 4) = 18$

5. Ben's family left for vacation after his dad came home from work on Friday. The entire trip was 600 mi. Dad was very tired after working a long day and decided to stop and spend the night in a hotel after 4 hours of driving. The next morning, Dad drove the remainder of the trip. If the average speed of the car was 60 miles per hour, what was the remaining time left to drive on the second part of the trip? Remember: Distance = rate multiplied by time.

Lesson Summary

We work backward to solve an algebraic equation. For example, to find the value of the variable in the equation $6x - 8 = 40$:

1. Use the addition property of equality to add the opposite of -8 to each side of the equation to arrive at
   $6x - 8 + 8 = 40 + 8$.
2. Use the additive inverse property to show that $-8 + 8 = 0$; thus, $6x + 0 = 48$.
3. Use the additive identity property to arrive at $6x = 48$.
4. Then use the multiplication property of equality to multiply both sides of the equation by $\frac{1}{6}$ to get:
   $\left(\frac{1}{6}\right) 6x = \left(\frac{1}{6}\right) 48$.
5. Then use the multiplicative inverse property to show that $\frac{1}{6}(6) = 1$; thus, $1x = 8$.
6. Use the multiplicative identity property to arrive at $x = 8$.

Problem Set

For each problem below, explain the steps in finding the value of the variable. Then find the value of the variable, showing each step. Write if–then statements to justify each step in solving the equation.

1. $7(m + 5) = 21$

2. $-2v + 9 = 25$

3. $\frac{1}{3}y - 18 = 2$

4. $6 - 8p = 38$

5. $15 = 5k - 13$

©2016 Great Minds. eureka-math.org
G7-M1M2-SE-B1-1.3.1-02.2016

This page intentionally left blank

Lesson 23: Solving Equations Using Algebra

Classwork

Exercises

1.   Youth Group Trip

The youth group is going on a trip to an amusement park in another part of the state. The trip costs each group member $150, which includes $85 for the hotel and two one-day combination entrance and meal plan passes.

a.   Write an equation representing the cost of the trip. Let P be the cost of the park pass.

b.   Solve the equation algebraically to find the cost of the park pass. Then write the reason that justifies each step using if-then statements.

c.   Model the problem using a tape diagram to check your work.

Suppose you want to buy your favorite ice cream bar while at the amusement park and it costs $2.89. If you purchase the ice cream bar and 3 bottles of water, pay with a $10 bill, and receive no change, then how much did each bottle of water cost?

d.   Write an equation to model this situation.

e.   Solve the equation to determine the cost of one water bottle. Then write the reason that justifies each step using if-then statements.

f.   Model the problem using a tape diagram to check your work.

©2016 Great Minds. eureka-math.org
G7-M1M2-SE-B1-1.3.1-02.2016

2. Weekly Allowance

Charlotte receives a weekly allowance from her parents. She spent half of this week's allowance at the movies, but earned an additional $4 for performing extra chores. If she did not spend any additional money and finished the week with $12, what is Charlotte's weekly allowance?

   a. Write an equation that can be used to find the original amount of Charlotte's weekly allowance. Let A be the value of Charlotte's original weekly allowance.

   b. Solve the equation to find the original amount of allowance. Then write the reason that justifies each step using if-then statements.

   c. Explain your answer in the context of this problem.

A STORY OF RATIOS

Lesson 23 7•2

d. Charlotte's goal is to save $100 for her beach trip at the end of the summer. Use the amount of weekly allowance you found in part (c) to write an equation to determine the number of weeks that Charlotte must work to meet her goal. Let w represent the number of weeks.

e. In looking at your answer to part (d) and based on the story above, do you think it will take Charlotte that many weeks to meet her goal? Why or why not?

3. Travel Baseball Team

Allen is very excited about joining a travel baseball team for the fall season. He wants to determine how much money he should save to pay for the expenses related to this new team. Players are required to pay for uniforms, travel expenses, and meals.

a. If Allen buys 4 uniform shirts at one time, he gets a $10.00 discount so that the total cost of 4 shirts would be $44. Write an algebraic equation that represents the regular price of one shirt. Solve the equation. Write the reason that justifies each step using if-then statements.

S.140   Lesson 23:   Solve Equations Using Algebra

EUREKA
MATH™

©2016 Great Minds. eureka-math.org
G7-M1M2-SE-B1-1.3.1-02.2016

b.   What is the cost of one shirt without the discount?

c.   What is the cost of one shirt with the discount?

d.   How much more do you pay per shirt if you buy them one at a time (rather than in bulk)?

Allen's team was also required to buy two pairs of uniform pants and two baseball caps, which total $68. A pair of pants costs $12 more than a baseball cap.

e.   Write an equation that models this situation. Let c represent the cost of a baseball cap.

f. Solve the equation algebraically to find the cost of a baseball cap. Write the reason that justifies each step using if-then statements.

g. Model the problem using a tape diagram in order to check your work from part (f).

h. What is the cost of one cap?

i. What is the cost of one pair of pants?

EUREKA
MATH

Lesson Summary

Equations are useful to model and solve real-world problems. The steps taken to solve an algebraic equation are the same steps used in an arithmetic solution.

Problem Set

For Exercises 1–4, solve each equation algebraically using if-then statements to justify your steps.

1. $\frac{2}{3}x - 4 = 20$

2. $4 = \frac{-1+x}{2}$

3. $12(x + 9) = -108$

4. $5x + 14 = -7$

For Exercises 5–7, write an equation to represent each word problem. Solve the equation showing the steps and then state the value of the variable in the context of the situation.

5. A plumber has a very long piece of pipe that is used to run city water parallel to a major roadway. The pipe is cut into two sections. One section of pipe is 12 ft. shorter than the other. If $\frac{3}{4}$ of the length of the shorter pipe is 120 ft., how long is the longer piece of the pipe?

6. Bob's monthly phone bill is made up of a $10 fee plus $0.05 per minute. Bob's phone bill for July was $22. Write an equation to model the situation using m to represent the number of minutes. Solve the equation to determine the number of phone minutes Bob used in July.

7. Kym switched cell phone plans. She signed up for a new plan that will save her $3.50 per month compared to her old cell phone plan. The cost of the new phone plan for an entire year is $294. How much did Kym pay per month under her old phone plan?

This page intentionally left blank

Notes

Notes

Notes

Notes

Notes

Notes